Carpentry for the Building Trades

Carpentry

FOR THE BUILDING TRADES

E. A. LAIR

Instructor in Building Trades, Jacksonville High School
Jacksonville, Illinois

SECOND EDITION

McGraw-Hill Book Company, Inc.

NEW YORK   TORONTO   LONDON

CARPENTRY FOR THE BUILDING TRADES

Second Printing

PREFACE

The aim of this book is to provide in text form the essentials of practical carpentry for the building trades; to bring into organized form the fundamental objectives of the construction of the small and the medium-sized frame house; and to provide a definite course for high school, technical school, vocational school, apprenticeship, and veterans' apprenticeship classes in carpentry.

Not only are the necessary trade procedures explained in about their regular order of occurrence but much related information is included, especially on certain phases of structural design. Design and selection of columns, beams, and other necessary members of the building are made easy with the use of tables, charts, and formulas prepared for this purpose.

Modern-type architecture has brought into use many new and different methods of construction not common in the past. Construction used in the basementless house, the ranch-type house, in picture windows, dry-wall construction, flat roofs, new methods of insulation and ventilation, plus many new materials never before used extensively, are equally treated here.

Estimating of materials, which is so essential to the building trades, has not been overlooked. Practical methods used by the tradesmen are employed in estimating various materials, such as lumber, flooring, siding, shingles, insulation, and many others. Easy-to-understand examples for each are given, using simple mathematics.

The author has departed completely from the old methods of building small carpentry models, so often used, because the student, apprentice, or craftsman who is to earn his living in this trade will need to know it as it is actually performed today. From more than thirty years' experience as a teacher and a tradesman, the author has tried to use and keep foremost in mind the knowledge and the operations in the field of carpentry that seem most essential for any desiring to secure employment as an advanced apprentice.

It is possible to construct a modified-sized building made from materials of standard dimensions in the school shop. This may be torn down and a large amount of the material used over again. A building of this type provides opportunity for training in such jobs as placing sills and joists; putting up studs and plates; cutting and installing rafters, siding, and sheathing; setting window and door frames—in fact, all the jobs that are found in frame-house construction. However, the best type of training is to have an actual house under construction, for, although various kinds of jobs and projects may offer many ways of teaching fundamentals, actual work on construction for customers will develop the skill and provide the essentials necessary to the training of the student and apprentice in carpentry for the building trades.

The author's intention was to make the material flexible enough to allow teachers to broaden the scope of the course in some cases and lessen it in others, as the situation in various localities and available equipment demand. Probably the most satisfactory accomplishment of the desired objectives can be attained by those students who have completed at least two semesters of woodwork.

E. A. LAIR

CONTENTS

1

FRAMING

Many of the following operations cannot be taught except as they are actually worked out and developed on a building project. Actual house building will fill this requirement. An effort should be made not only to gain a knowledge of construction but to develop skill in the use of carpentry tools. After these have been attained, strive for speed, accuracy, and neatness.

TOOLS

There are many makes of carpentry tools on the market. Some of them are very good; some, very poor. None of them is efficient unless kept clean and in good working order. Plane blades should be kept sharp. Saws should be well shaped, and hammer handles should be kept tight. The proper care and condition of his tools are the first essentials of a skilled and efficient mechanic.

The tool chest of the building trades student should consist of the following:

>1 ripsaw
>1 crosscut saw

1 jack plane
1 ratchet brace
1 set auger bits, Nos. 4 to 16
1 countersink
1 marking gage
1 sliding T bevel, 8 in.
1 miter square, 8 in.
1 steel square, 24 in. (with rafter table)
2 screw drivers, 6 in. and 12 in.
1 screw-driver bit
1 pliers (wire cutting)
1 mallet
4 wood chisels, $\frac{1}{4}$ in., $\frac{1}{2}$ in., 1 in., $1\frac{1}{2}$ in.
1 saw vise
2 8-in. slim taper files
1 10-in. flat mill file
1 12-in. half-round wood file
1 pair of 8-in. dividers
1 6-ft. steel or aluminum rule
1 28-in. aluminum level
1 hammer—straight claws—16 oz.
1 oilstone
2 nail sets, $\frac{1}{16}$ in. and $\frac{1}{8}$ in.
1 coping saw
1 compass saw
1 Yankee drill with bits
1 backsaw
1 chalk line and chalk
1 tin snips
1 hatchet

JOINTS

It is necessary that the building trades student be able not only to use and care for his tools, but also to make the various joints and construction details commonly found in the building of a house, before being assigned to work on any building of importance.

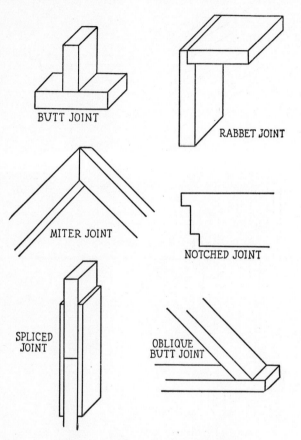

Figure 1. Joints in common use.

Braced framing of houses has been almost completely replaced today by balloon framing and western framing. However, there are still a number of joints in common use, as shown in Figure 1.

TYPES OF FRAMING

There are three types of framing for small-house construction, commonly known as (1) balloon framing, (2) western framing (platform), and (3) braced framing. Regardless of the type of framing, each must be strong and rigid and sturdy. Long durability

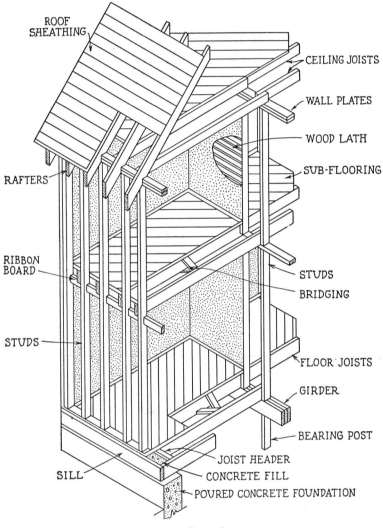

Figure 2. Balloon framing.

and resistance to wind, tornado, earthquakes, settling, and twisting must all depend upon a strong, well-built frame.

General opinion may vary as to which is the best type of construction, but part of the question can be settled by certain factors, such as the materials obtainable, the locality, and the climate. For example, a house built in that part of the country where strong winds prevail would probably call for braced framing.

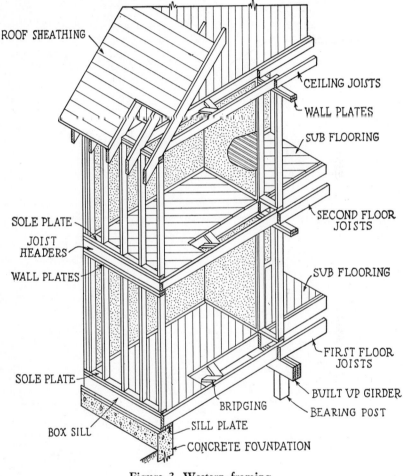

ROOF SHEATHING

CEILING JOISTS

WALL PLATES

SUB FLOORING

SOLE PLATE

JOIST HEADERS

WALL PLATES

SECOND FLOOR JOISTS

SUB FLOORING

FIRST FLOOR JOISTS

SOLE PLATE

BRIDGING

BUILT UP GIRDER

BEARING POST

BOX SILL

SILL PLATE

CONCRETE FOUNDATION

Figure 3. Western framing.

Balloon framing. Balloon framing is a term given to that type of construction in which the framework of the building is spiked together with butt joints. It depends largely for its strength upon the exterior covering or boxing and upon the manner in which it is applied. Another characteristic is the use of studs extending in one piece from the foundation to the roof. The joist ends are nailed to

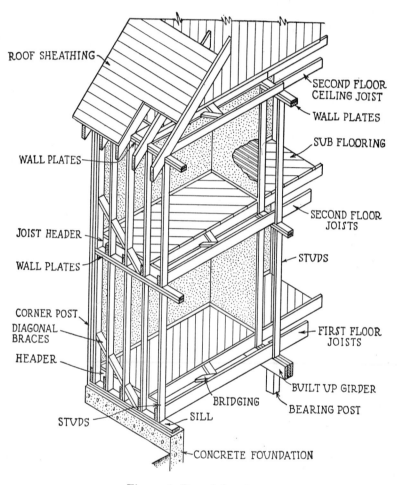

ROOF SHEATHING

SECOND FLOOR CEILING JOIST

WALL PLATES

SUB FLOORING

WALL PLATES

SECOND FLOOR JOISTS

JOIST HEADER

WALL PLATES

STUDS

CORNER POST
DIAGONAL BRACES

FIRST FLOOR JOISTS

HEADER

BUILT UP GIRDER

BRIDGING

BEARING POST

STUDS

SILL

CONCRETE FOUNDATION

Figure 4. Braced framing.

the studs and are supported on a ribbon or ledger board which has been let into the studs (Figure 2).

Western framing. Western framing, sometimes called "platform" framing, is a term given to that type of construction in which the framework of the building is built up in floors, or one story at a time. Each floor is independently framed. The second story and the third are supported by studs only one story high. This type is usually easier for the apprentice because short pieces are generally used. Another merit lies in the fact that, if any shrinkage occurs, it is likely to be uniform throughout and so is unnoticeable (Figure 3).

Braced framing. Braced framing is a term given to the type of construction that is characterized by heavy timbers at the corners, often with intermediate posts, all of which extend continuously from a heavy foundation sill to an equally heavy plate at the roof line. Most of the joints are mortised, and some are fastened with pins. Knee braces are used at the corners and are notched in at the plates and corner posts.

This is perhaps the oldest type of framing, having been brought to this country from England. However, it has been gradually modified, and timbers have been reduced in size. Originally the studs were only fillers, to which the lath and plaster were nailed. They supported nothing else. At present, however, they are an integral part of the structure and act to support the floors, roofs, etc., similar to other types of framing (Figure 4).

TYPE JOBS

The type jobs listed below have been selected because of their constant recurrence in frame-house construction. It is our purpose here to give the student certain technical information that can be coupled with his practical experience on the job under the direction of the trade teacher. An honest attempt should be made to execute the practical processes without violating technical factors. The following type jobs are listed about in the order in which they would be brought into construction on a building.

LAYOUT AND SITE

Levels. It is most important in preparing a site for the erection of any building that one predetermine a definite imaginary reference line or level for the start of the construction. For example, any building should be built at an elevation that provides easy access to the main floor from the streets or walks. This line may be at the grade level, foundation top, or the first floor level. Thus, after it has been established, the builder can build up or down from this line. In many cities, bench marks are provided by the city or local engineering offices. If architects' plans are used they will definitely show these locations. These marks usually consist of a mark, or point, on

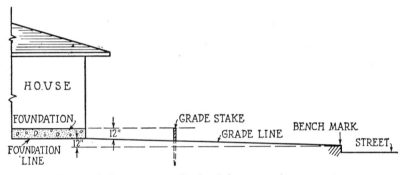

Figure 5. Determining the level for start of construction.

the foundation of some other building, or a stone marker sometimes buried at a designated location. Quite often they are taken from sidewalk and street levels. Street curbs are used extensively, as it is a general practice to establish a grade line around a house a given number of inches higher than the street curb (Figure 5). It is usually necessary in new sections of a city, where bench marks and street curbs are not to be found, to have the running of levels performed by an engineer. This safeguards the builder and ensures the proper elevation in case of subsequent street extension and sidewalk construction.

Location of building. Next in importance to proper elevations is the exact location of the building on the lot. The size of the lot and the amount of distance to be left on each side of the house to the property line must be determined. If the property lines are not known, it will be necessary to employ a surveyor to determine and lay out the boundaries of the lot. The corners of the lot are then marked with a steel pin, or peg, driven into the ground. Most cities have local codes and regulations covering many things in regard to the location of a building on a lot.

The builder should be familiar with these regulations as well as with others that might apply, such as Federal Housing Administration's (F.H.A.) regulations, in cases where this agency is concerned. Local codes often determine the distances from the street or the sidewalk to the house, the minimum amount of side yard allowed, kinds of driveways, their location, etc. The F.H.A. and other financing agencies inject many other requirements into the planning and placing of the house on the lot.

Staking out the house. If the building to be built is a residence, it will probably be surrounded by a lawn or a yard and be set back from the street a certain distance. If the building is not set parallel with the street or the property line, it will need to be laid out by an engineer or with an engineer's transit if it is to face a given direction. Figure 6 shows a simple method for laying out the site if it is to be parallel with the property lines or the street. First, measure back from the street on the side lines of the lot the distance A, desired to the front of the house. Then stretch a tight line from point X to X. This establishes line B, or the front of the building. To obtain the front corners of the building, measure in on line B from the sides of the lot the desired distances, taking into account the actual length of the house. This determines the actual distances C and D. The rear wall line, or line F, will be parallel to line B and distances E will be alike and represent the width of the house. If the building is not rectangular, it may be necessary to run several lines across the lot. After these points have been found at the corners of the excavation or the foundation, stakes should be driven at each corner or angle. From these stakes batter boards may be erected and dimensions may be determined accurately and checked with those on the blueprints or plans.

Batter boards. Before any building construction is started, the ground must be excavated, either for the basement or for the trenches for the foundation. Excavation will naturally disturb the pegs driven at the corners of the foundation during the first layout. Therefore it is necessary to set up, at each corner or angle, batter boards (Figure 7). These are erected in order that lines of heavy

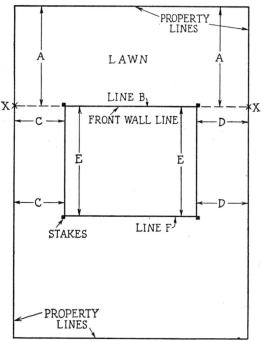

Figure 6. After this layout has been acquired, batter boards may be erected to obtain accurate measurements for the building.

cord or fine wire may be stretched from one to another for the purpose of obtaining accurate measurements and providing a definite line to work toward. These lines are very essential to all footing and foundation construction.

To construct the batter boards, heavy stakes are set into the ground about 6 to 8 ft. away from the actual excavation and about 8 to 10 ft. apart. These stakes may be of wood 2 by 4's, 2 by 6's, or even 4 by 4's. They should be heavy and sturdy enough to withstand ordinary working conditions around the house without being damaged or pushed out of line. The boards are then nailed or bolted onto the stakes at the exact height and level of the top of the foundation. When these have been prepared at each corner, the lines may then be stretched. Stretch the lines tightly and adjust them by slipping them in either direction on the batter boards.

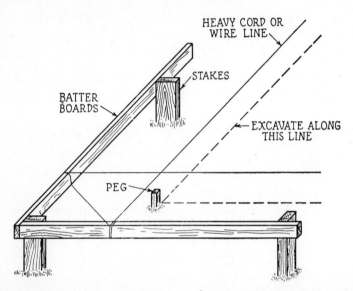

Figure 7. Batter boards are erected for excavation work. Note how easily the lines may be moved for an adjustment. Saw marks may be placed along the top of these boards to indicate the building line, footings line, excavating line, or others.

After final adjustments have been made for accuracy and square-ness, saw cuts may be made in the top edges of the boards just deep enough to hold the lines and keep them from being moved out of place. Various cuts may be used to indicate the building line, founda-tion line, footings line, and excavation line. By use of the saw cuts the lines may also be removed and then replaced in their correct location.

Squaring the foundation. There are several ways to arrive at a perfectly square layout. However, two generally accepted methods are those commonly used by the carpenter. The first is called the

6-8-10 method (Figure 8). After the batter boards are up and the lines are in place, they can be checked for squareness. By this method an adjustment can be continued until an absolute right angle has been obtained. The distances 6 ft., 8 ft., and 10 ft. may be used or any multiple thereof. For example, measure off the distance from

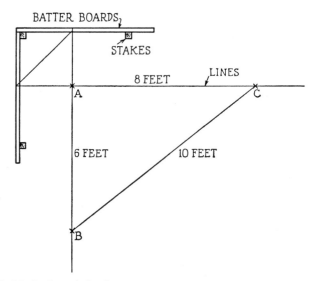

Figure 8. Method used for laying out a square corner for a building or for excavation work.

A to *B* with a steel tape. Let this distance be exactly 6 ft. Then measure off the distance from *A* to *C*. Let this distance be exactly 8 ft. Adjust the lines now until the distance from *B* to *C* is exactly 10 ft.

The second method is called the "diagonal" method (Figure 9). This method is commonly used when the shape of the building permits. For example, find the length of line *E*, or the hypotenuse of the triangle *ABC*. Then check the distances from *A* to *D* and from *B* to *C*. The distances will be the same if the layout is square. If it is not square, adjust corners at *C* and *D* by moving both to the right or to the left.

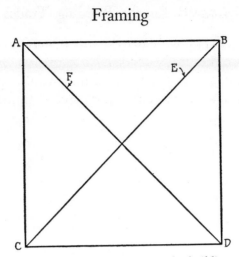

Figure 9. The diagonal method is also used in the building trades for laying out square corners, but it is more commonly used for checking squareness.

FOOTINGS

Definition. Regardless of the type of framing employed or of how rigidly the frame is built, if an inadequate foundation is provided the frame will probably settle unevenly. This uneven settlement will result in the cracking of plaster, tile, and floors, and in ill-fitting doors and sticking windows. Wall footings and post or column footings are sometimes figured undersize; and in some cases of poor or cheap construction, they are left out entirely. Footings are the widened sections of the foundation base designed to increase the area of the bearing surface of the bottom of the foundation. The size of the footing is determined first by the resistive qualities or firmness of the soil and, second, by the weight which must be supported. The heavier the weight the foundation must support, the larger the foundation must be; and the softer the soil, the larger the footings must be. Most footings can be grouped into the following types: (1) wall footings, (2) column footings, (3) pier footings, (4) chimney footings, (5) pilaster footings, (6) porch and stair footings, (7) wall-projection footings.

Purpose. The purpose of footings is to distribute the foundation load over a greater soil area without any sinking or settling into the soil in which they are placed. While the foundation supports the building or structure above it, the footings in turn support the foundation and, in turn, the soil supports the footings. It is possible for a building with inadequate footings to sink or settle far enough to cause it to collapse. It is for this reason that the strength or firmness of the soil must be considered when a building is being planned, so as not to overload the soil per square foot.

TABLE 1. SAFE LOADS FOR VARIOUS SOILS

Type of soil	Safe load, tons per square foot
Loam..................	1
Soft clay...............	1
Hard clay..............	2
Dry fine sand...........	2
Compact coarse sand......	3
Coarse gravel...........	4
Hard pan or shale........	6
Solid rock..............	No limit

Spacing. Therefore, the load on each footing should be carefully figured and the footings be made large enough to carry loads per square foot not to exceed those given in Table 1.

Construction. In all cases, excavations for all footings should be be made well under the frost line. In cold climates this is usually considered to be from 3 to 4 ft. deep and, in extreme northern sections of the country, 4 to 6 ft. deep. Because of the possibility of settling, no permanent building should be erected over any fresh fill, and in extreme cases, if such is necessary, an engineer or an architect should be consulted before any work is started. Of course, where basements are used, the depth of the footing is determined by the depth of the basement and the amount of foundation showing above the grade line. Distribution of the foundation load is shown in Figures 10 and 11. Figure 10 shows a cross section of a foundation without any footings. The foundation is 12 in. thick and 7 ft. in height. We will

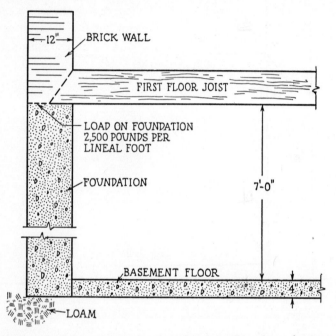

Figure 10. Cross section of a foundation wall without footings.

assume the load on the foundation from the building it supports to be 2,500 lb. per lineal foot. Concrete weighs approximately 150 lb. per cu. ft., thus a lineal foot of this foundation would weigh 150 lb. times 7, or 1,050 lb. This weight added to that which the foundation must support makes a total of 3,550 lb. per lineal foot that the soil must support.

By consulting Table 1, we find that loam or soft clay will obviously not support this, and the foundation will probably sink or settle if built on it. Thus other provisions would need to be made. This can be done by widening the footings sufficiently on the bottom, which in turn will decrease the load per square foot to the extent that clay or loam will support the load without sinking or settling. A cross section of the same wall with sufficient footings added is shown in Figure 11.

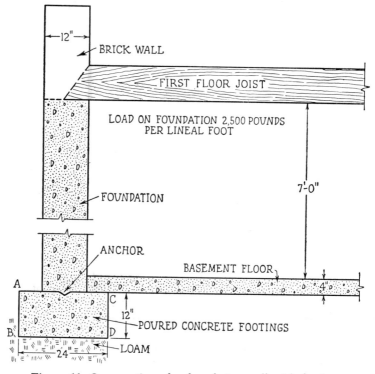

Figure 11. Cross section of a foundation wall with footings.

Distribution of the foundation load has been made over a greater soil area. *ABCD* represents the section of footing added. In order to find the necessary area per lineal foot needed to support the foundation without any settling or sinking, we will need to divide the load, 3,550 lb., by the safe load per square foot soil (2,000 lb.). Thus 3,550 divided by 2,000 equals 1.775 sq. ft. As this is approximately 2 sq. ft., it can be assumed that the load of the foundation will be distributed over this area. Therefore, the load from the foundation when distributed over 2 sq. ft. of surface amounts to 1,775 lb. per sq. ft. According to Table 1, this is less than the maximum strength or firmness of the soil, thus the foundation and the building will not settle.

Footings for pier posts, columns, and bearing posts have the same purpose as the footings for foundation walls. Their sizes are deter-

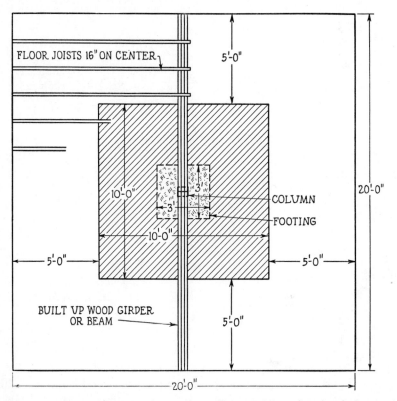

Figure 12. The column in the center will support one-fourth of the total weight of the building. Sometimes this footing may be required to support ten times as much per square foot as the wall footings.

mined in much the same way. However, these footings carry a much greater load per square foot of bearing surface than do the foundation walls. For example, in Figure 12 we have a house 20 ft. square, with one girder or beam and one column set on the footing. All the weight of the building over the shaded area will fall on this footing, or one-fourth of the total weight. If we assume the weight of the building to be 72,000 lb., then the weight to be carried by the footing would be 18,000 lb. This, of course, would be the same as 9 tons. With the same soil conditions as above, the safe load per square foot of soil would be 2,000 lb. Thus 9 sq. ft. of surface would be needed. To determine the dimensions of the sides of this footing, it would be necessary to take the square root of 9. This answer would be 3. Thus the footing would need to be 3 ft. square. The depth of a footing is usually determined by taking one-half the length of one side. For example, a footing 3 ft. square would be 18 in. deep.

COLUMNS

Definition. Columns, sometimes called "bearing posts" in frame-house construction, are vertical members designed and placed to

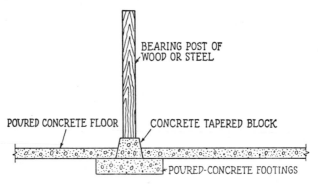

Figure 13. The bearing post should rest on a concrete tapered block which in turn rests on a poured-concrete footing.

carry their share of the load, or the weight of the house. They directly support the girders or beams and these, in turn, are supported by the column foundation and footing. In frame-house construction they are usually made of wood. However, there are many kinds. They may be steel I beams, steel H beams, steel Lally columns, brick, block, etc. In each case where columns are to be used, the situation should be carefully studied and the type of column selected which best meets all the conditions encountered. Because of their great strength, ability to withstand abuse and hard use, the small space required for installation, low cost and availability, wood columns are deserving of more general use than is common (Figure 13).

Sizes. The size of the column should depend on the load it will be expected to carry, as well as the length or height it must be. Thus the length of a column will be the distance from the basement floor up to the underside of the beam which will rest on top of the column. This is known as the effective length, or unbraced length,

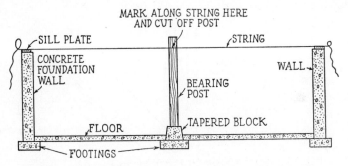

Figure 14. To obtain the exact length of a bearing post.

of the column. Wood columns may be made from any one of several kinds of wood. The strength of these woods varies accordingly. These factors must always be taken into consideration when the size of a column is computed. Obviously, hardwood will make stronger columns than softwood. There are several methods for finding the exact lengths of a column and, where this has not been predetermined, a simple and accurate method is that shown in Figure 14.

The exact length of a wood column may be determined by stretching a tight line from the top of one wall foundation to the top of the other, with a slight allowance for sag in the line. Another much-used method is to sight from one side to another while a mark is made on the column at the right height. It is very important that both top and bottom cuts on the columns be square, in order to provide an even bearing surface for the beam and a level seat on the tapered block or footing. When tapered concrete blocks are used, as in Figure 13, water cannot get to the bottom of the wood post and cause rotting.

Construction. It is very desirable that columns be secured to the foundation block in some manner, to prevent possible dislodgment

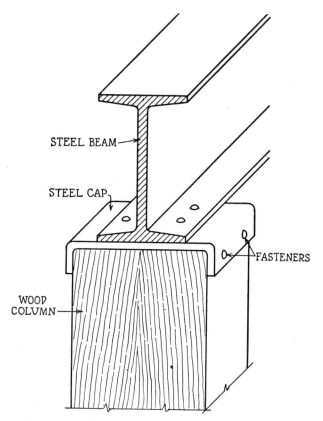

Figure 15. If a wood column supports a steel beam, a metal cap should be provided at the top.

from a heavy blow or shock. This is particularly important for columns used in garages or in basements. It is done by inserting into the concrete block an iron anchor bolt, about $\frac{1}{2}$ in. by 15 in., and allowing about 3 in. to extend into the end of the column. If the wood column supports a steel beam, a metal cap should be provided at the top to help distribute the load from the beam to the whole

area of the top of the column (Figure 15). It is also a good practice
to apply a thin coat or bed of mortar to the top of the tapered block
at the time the column is set. This provides an even bearing in case
the block is not exactly flat on top. Under no condition should the
column go below the floor or surface of the concrete or be placed
in any manner that would allow it to come in contact with the
earth.

Spacing. The type and size of beams used will determine the size
and spacing of the columns. Greater distances between columns

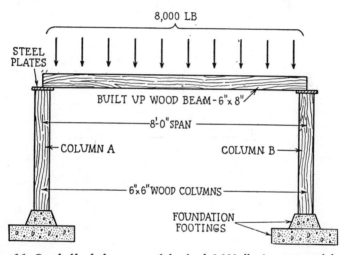

Figure 16. One-half of the assumed load of 8,000 lb. is supported by each
column.

usually require larger beams, which in turn cut down the headroom
in the basement. They also cause greater concentration of weight on
both the column and the foundation. Spans for columns in ordinary
frame-house construction should seldom be more than 8 ft. on center. The first step necessary in determining the size of a column is
to find the load it must carry. The column supports the beam, so
it must support, as well, the weight brought to it by the beam.

Thus a column will carry the load on a beam to the mid-point
of the span on both sides. A beam having an equally distributed
load and supported at its ends, as shown in Figure 16, in turn dis-

tributes half of its load to each column. Therefore, half of the assumed 8,000 lb., or 4,000 lb., is supported by column *A* and the other half, or 4,000 lb., is supported by column *B*. Each of these 4,000-lb. loads is a concentrated load so far as the columns are concerned, because the beam causes the loads to fall at one point. In this case it is the end of the column. If this 8,000 lb. represented the weight of the first floor, it might well be increased three times or more when the weight of the second floor, attic, floors, partitions, roofs, etc., were added. In that event, the concentrated load might be as much as 12,000 lb. on each column.

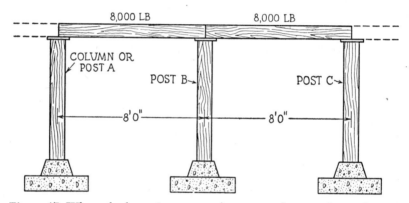

Figure 17. Where the beam is cut over the center column and on other supports on each side, the load on column *B* will be one-half the beam load from *A* to *B*, 4,000 lb. plus one-half the beam load from *B* to *C*, or 4,000 lb. Therefore, the total load for column *B* will be 8,000 lb.

Computing column loads. As previously stated, a column will carry the load on a beam to the mid-point of the span on both sides (Figure 17). This is true when all beams are cut over columns, but where built-up beams are used as one continuous beam, the weight will vary for the outside span. Figure 18 shows a type of wood-beam-and-column construction in common use. Here a single built-up beam is supported at four points equidistant. Column *B* can be assumed to carry five-eighths of the beam load from *A* to *B*, or 5,000 lb., and one-half the beam load from *B* to *C*, or 4,000 lb., thus carrying a load of 9,000 lb. Likewise, column *C* can be assumed to carry five-eighths of the beam load from C to D, or 5,000 lb., and one-half the beam load from C to B, or 4,000 lb., thus carrying a load of 9,000 lb.

When the load on each column has been determined, the next procedure is to find the size of column needed. In order to determine this, Table 2 may be used. From the column of figures on the left in the table, select the height of the column to be used. From this, follow the line across to the nearest figure representing the safe load in pounds allowed. For example, in Figure 18, column B must support 9,000 lb. If the column is to be 8 ft. long, and of Douglas

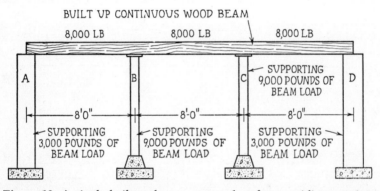

Figure 18. A single built-up beam supported at four equidistant points.

fir, follow the line across to the nearest figure listed over 9,000 lb., and we find it to be 12,950 lb. At the top of this column of figures we find that a wood column, size 4 by 6 in., would be needed. No column smaller than this should ever be used; even though a smaller one might be strong enough, to the average home builder it would not appear so.

Steel columns. Modern-type architecture has come to employ steel columns extensively. There are many reasons for this. When steel is used, smaller columns may suffice, and fewer will be needed (Figure 19). However, it is usually the job of the carpenter to install these on small construction, such as frame houses, apartments, barns, garages, etc. In order to find the correct size for these, it is necessary merely to follow the same procedure as that for wood columns,

TABLE 2. MAXIMUM ALLOWANCE LOADS IN POUNDS
FOR WOOD COLUMNS

Height of column, feet	Nominal size, inches				Grade and kind of wood
	4 × 6	6 × 6	6 × 8	8 × 8	
	Actual size, inches				
	3⅝ × 5⅝	5½ × 5½	5½ × 7½	7½ × 7½	
	Area, square inches				
	20.39	30.25	41.25	56.25	
4	19,850	30,250	41,250	56,250	No. 1 Common
5	19,200	30,050	41,000	56,250	Douglas fir
6	17,950	29,500	40,260	56,250	Southern pine
7	15,550	29,000	39,600	55,650	North Carolina pine
8	12,950	28,150	38,300	55,000	
4	17,410	26,620	36,300	49,500	No. 1 Common
5	16,480	26,440	36,050	49,500	Red cypress
6	14,800	25,860	35,270	49,500	Red wood
7	12,210	25,050	34,150	49,050	
8	9,620	23,960	32,620	48,260	
4	14,500	21,780	29,700	40,500	No. 1 Common
5	14,110	21,720	29,620	40,500	West-coast hemlock
6	13,480	21,510	29,330	40,500	and tamarack
7	12,480	21,170	28,870	40,330	
8	10,870	20,750	28,300	40,050	
6	10,300	16,700	22,850	31,500	No. 1 Common
7	9,270	16,400	22,400	31,300	Eastern hemlock
8	7,930	15,950	21,800	31,000	White fir, white pine
					Spruce

except in the use of the tables. For steel I columns use Table 3. For steel H columns use Table 4. For steel Lally columns use Table 5.

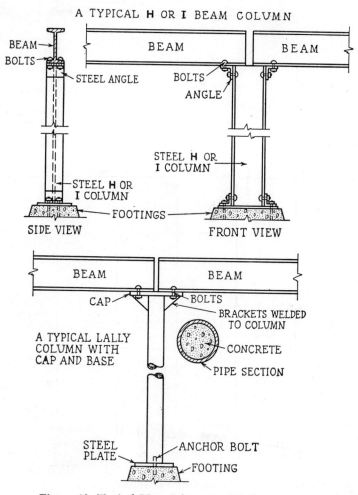

Figure 19. Typical H or I beam and Lally columns.

FOUNDATION SILLS

Definition. The foundation sill is a plank installed directly onto the foundation wall. It forms the base support for the outside frame

TABLE 3. STEEL BEAM COLUMNS.* SAFE LOADS IN THOUSANDS OF POUNDS

I Beams

Effective length, feet	Size, inches				
	8	7	6	5	4
	Weight, pounds per foot				
	18.4	15.3	12.5	10.0	7.7
3	69.3	57.5	46.9	37.3	28.5
4	69.3	57.6	44.4	33.5	24.0
5	63.3	49.9	38.3	28.2	19.5
6	55.7	43.1	32.3	22.9	15.2
7	48.1	36.2	26.2	18.9	13.0
8	40.5	30.2	22.7	16.3	10.8
9	35.1	26.8	19.7	13.6	8.5
10	31.3	23.4	16.7	11.0	6.3

* Allowable fiber stress per square inch, 13,000 lb. for lengths over 60 radii. Weights do not include details. Loads above the upper horizontal lines will produce maximum allowable shear in webs. Loads below the horizontal lines will produce excessive deflections. (*A.I.S.C. Handbook.*)

walls of the house. There are several general types of foundation sills. The type used will depend upon the general type of construction being used in the frame. A T-sill construction, commonly found and used in the dry, warm climates, is shown in Figure 20.

A foundation sill commonly used in the East is shown in Figure

TABLE 4. STEEL BEAM COLUMNS.* SAFE LOADS IN THOUSANDS OF POUNDS

H Beams

Effective length, feet	Size, inches							
	4	5	6			8		
	Weight, pounds per foot							
	13.8	18.9	22.8	24.1	26.7	32.6	34.3	37.7
3	51.9	71.1	86.2	91.1	100.9	123.6	130.0	143.0
4	51.9	71.1	86.2	91.1	100.9	123.6	130.0	143.0
5	50.5	71.1	86.2	91.1	100.9	123.6	130.0	143.0
6	45.5	71.1	86.2	91.1	100.9	123.6	130.0	143.0
7	40.4	65.6	86.2	91.1	100.9	123.6	130.0	143.0
8	35.3	60.1	82.5	86.7	95.1	123.6	130.0	143.0
9	30.3	54.6	77.1	80.9	88.5	123.6	130.0	143.0
10	26.6	49.1	71.7	75.1	80.0	120.5	126.0	136.9

* Allowable fiber stress per square inch, 13,000 lb. for lengths over 60 radii. Weights do not include details. Loads above the upper horizontal lines will produce maximum allowable shear in webs. Loads below the horizontal lines will produce excessive deflections. (*A.I.S.C. Handbook.*)

21. This construction is similar to the T sill, except that the joists are nailed directly to the studs, as well as to the sills, and headers are used between the floor joists. These headers act as draft and fire stops and also provide a nailing surface for the ends of the sub-flooring if nailed on diagonally. The very popular style of platform

TABLE 5. SAFE LOADS FOR STEEL LALLY COLUMNS IN THOUSANDS OF POUNDS *

Diameter of column, in.	Weight per foot, lb.	Area o steel, sq. in.	Area of concrete, sq. in.	Unbraced length of column, feet							
				6	7	8	9	10	11	12	13
3½	15	2.23	7.39	37.9	35.1	32.3	29.4	26.7	24.0		
4	20	2.68	9.89	49.2	46.1	43.1	40.1	37.0	33.9	30.9	27.9
4½	24	3.17	12.73	61.8	58.5	55.3	52.0	48.8	45.5	42.3	39.0
5	29	3.69	15.95	75.6	72.0	68.6	65.2	61.7	58.2	54.7	51.3
5½	36	4.30	20.01	92.1	88.3	84.6	80.8	77.1	73.3	69.6	65.8
6⅝	49	5.58	28.89	128.3	124.2	120	115.8				
7⅝	64	6.92	38.74	166.0	161.4	156.9					

* Lally Company Handbook.

framing with the box sill is shown in Figure 22. This style automatically fire-stops the walls and partitions at each level. It permits the subflooring to be laid readily at a diagonal if desired, which in

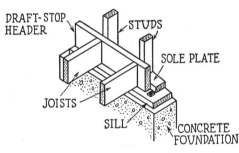

Figure 20. T-sill construction, southern assembly.

turn provides a platform on which to work in erecting the rest of the frame.

The foundation sill generally used in braced-framing construction is shown in Figure 23. This type of construction is the oldest known, originating in New England. The floor joists are notched out and are nailed directly to the sill and to the studs. The sills are usually 4 by 6's, or 4 by 8's. The recessed sill is shown in Figure 24.

This is comparatively new as general construction. This type of
sill was developed to enable the builder to obtain lower to the

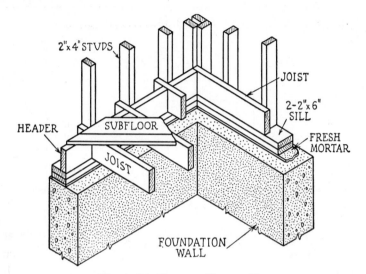

Figure 21. Eastern sill assembly.

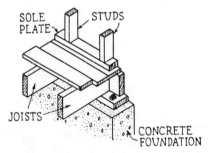 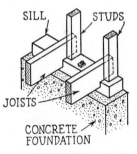

Figure 22. Popular platform box sill or
western sill assembly (western framing).

Figure 23. Sill commonly
used in braced framing.

ground floor levels, which are increasing rapidly in popularity. The
development of ranch-type architecture has been largely responsible
for its use. It can be used with a full basement plan or with a crawl-
space plan.

Wide acceptance of the basementless house has brought into use a different type of construction at the sill location, where solid-concrete slab floors are used (Figure 25). The slab floor eliminates the use of columns, beams, sills, and floor joists. Here, however, the sole plate actually becomes a sill and carries the outside frame wall.

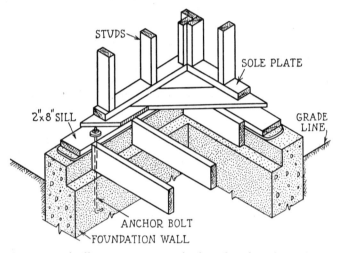

Figure 24. Recessed sill construction, used where low foundations are wanted.

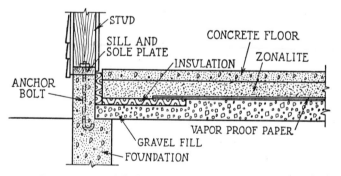

Figure 25. Where concrete slab floors are used, the sole plate actually becomes a sill.

Sizes. Sills vary in size according to the width of the foundation and the amount of weight to be carried, but for frame-house construction, 2 by 6's and 2 by 8's are generally used. In braced framing, the sills are usually 4 in. thick and well anchored to the foundation. The 4-in. sills also afford more nailing surface when the wall sheathing is nailed on diagonally. In some sections of the country where the building may be supported on columns, the sill sizes would need to be increased, as in that case they would actually be serving as beams and would need to be figured as such. Nearly any good grade of No. 1 common wood may be suitable for sills, inasmuch as the sill will have uniform bearing surface around the top of the foundation.

Construction. All sill timber should be fairly straight, well seated or imbedded in mortar, and anchored to the foundation. The length

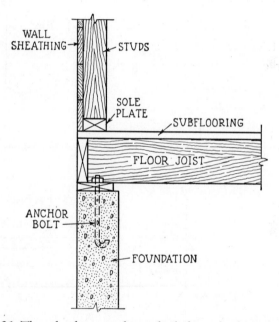

Figure 26. The sole plate may be set back from the face of the sill.

of the sill is determined by the size of the foundation. As the size of a building is usually calculated in dimensions taken to the outside face of the wall sheathing, the sills will need to be set back ¾ in. from the face of the foundation wall if the sheathing is to come down over the face of the sills. However, in box-sill construction, the sill may be set flush with the foundation and the sole plate set back ¾ in. instead. Thus the sheathing would come down only to the subflooring, as shown in Figure 26. In splicing for lengths, butt joints may be used if they are well made, and should be toenailed together. If more than one course is used, the joints should be staggered and not made over each other.

All sills should be well anchored to the foundation. This is done by setting into the foundation, at the proper time, anchor bolts. These bolts are usually installed at the time the foundation is built. The type of foundation will determine the size of the bolts needed. For poured-concrete foundations, bolts of size ½ in. by 10 or 12 in. will do. For hollow tile, concrete block, etc., the bolts will need to be at least ½ in. by 18 in. and well bedded with mortar in the hollow parts of the block or tile. A bolt should project up through the sill far enough to receive a washer and a nut. Anchor bolts should be placed at least 8 ft. on center and also 12 in. back from all corners and openings.

Termite protection. In just about all localities it is necessary to provide some form of protection to the house from termite destruc-

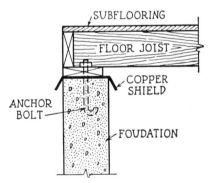

Figure 27. A copper shield should be placed around the top of the foundation under the sills. This acts as termite protection. The shield should be bent down as shown.

tion. One method is the application of various kinds of oils made and sold for this purpose. They can usually be purchased at the local lumberyards. The sills and various framing members are either painted or dipped with this oil before being placed. Another method of protection is the use of the copper shield. The shield is placed on top of the foundation and is left extending on each side for a distance of about 1½ in. This overhang of the shield should be bent down slightly (Figure 27). Various weights of copper sheeting may be used or a copper-coated paper made for this purpose may be installed. Whichever is used, it should be rigid enough to hold the required shape. If the copper-coated paper is chosen, the copper side should be placed down, or against the foundation.

BEAMS

Definition. Beams, sometimes called "girders" in frame-house construction, are structural pieces of timber or iron used for supporting loads in the absence of walls or bearing partitions. Their installation is usually the carpenter's job, whether they be steel or of wood. When beams are used in house construction, their ends usually rest on the foundation walls and their middles are supported by bearing posts, called "columns." This eliminates the necessity for bearing walls or partitions in the basement or other places where they might not be wanted. These beams and their supporting columns carry a relatively large part of the weight of the building.

All structures that have been designed by an architect will have stated on the blueprints and in the specifications the kind and size of beams to be used. However, it is often necessary for the carpenter and the builder to decide what size and type of beam should be used. There are several factors that determine these things—first of all, the computing of the load they must carry. Next it is necessary to decide whether the beam is to be of wood or of steel, and if of wood, the kind or species to be used. When these matters have been determined, finding the size needed is not difficult.

Purpose. The purpose of a beam is to support the inner ends of the floor joists (Figure 28). There are *three* general classes of wood beams: (1) built-up wood beam, (2) solid or one-piece wood beam,

(3) built-up wood and steel beams. Built-up wood beams are usually made by spiking together two or more 2 by 8's, or other-sized pieces

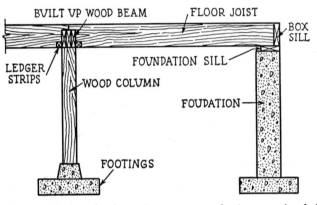

Figure 28. The purpose of a beam is to support the inner ends of the floor joists. Above is a floor joist and beam arrangement.

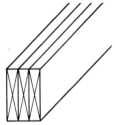

Figure 29. Built-up girders are usually made by spiking together three pieces as shown. Pieces should be well nailed, and all joints made over the bearing posts.

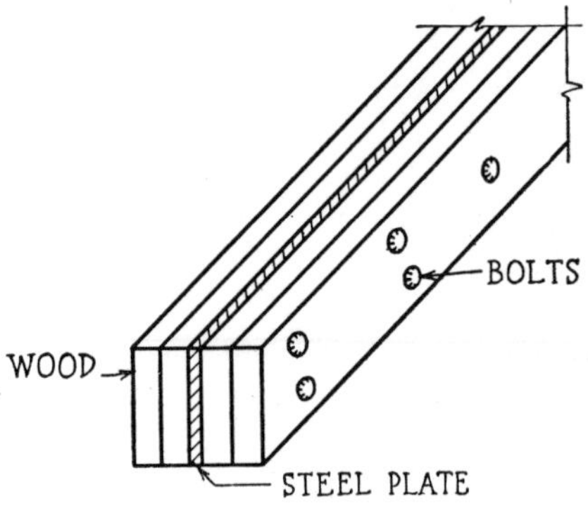

Figure 30. A built-up wood and steel beam, commonly called the "flitched" beam.

(Figure 29). Solid, or one-piece, beams can be purchased in the needed sizes from the local lumberyards. These are usually in such sizes as 4 by 6's, 4 by 8's, 4 by 10's, 6 by 6's, 6 by 8's, 6 by 10's, etc. The built-up wood and steel beam (Figure 30) is, as a rule, made by using 2 by 8's or other sizes of wood bolted together with a steel plate in the middle. This beam is commonly called the "flitched" beam.

Sizes. To determine the size of a beam, the following steps are necessary.

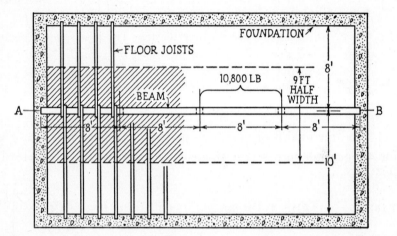

Figure 31. To determine the "half width" for a beam, take the distance from the center line of the beam to the nearest joist support on one side. This distance is known as the "floor-joist" span. Add to this figure the corresponding span or a distance from a center line of the beam to the nearest beam or wall on the other side. One-half of this total is known as the "half width." If the joists are continuous, five-eighths of the total will equal the "half width."

1. Decide upon the length of the beam between supports. This means that the columns supporting the beam must be spaced to some suitable division of the total length or distance between the foundation walls. Excessive spans should be avoided, and recommended practice suggests distances approximately 8 ft. on center. This also meets the approval of the F.H.A. when used in frame-house construction. As you will see, short spans reduce the size of the beam and increase the headroom in the basement.

2. Determine the "half widths." To determine the half width for a beam, take the distance from the center line of the beam to the nearest joist support on one side. This distance is known as

the floor-joist span. Add to this figure the corresponding span or distance from the center line of the beam to the nearest beam or wall on the other side. One-half of this total is the half width, provided that the joists are lapped or butted over the beam. If the joists are continuous, five-eighths of the total will equal the "half width."

> *Example* (Figure 31): Here the beam is continuous from *A* to *B*, with the joists lapped over the top. The joist spans are 8 ft. on one side and 10 ft. on the other, or a total of 18 ft. One-half of this total, or 9 ft., would be the "half width." If the floor joists were continuous, the half width would be five-eighths of 18 ft., or 11¼ ft.

3. Find the total floor load per square foot. Table 6 may be used for all general purposes in frame-house construction where total minimum square-foot floor loads are needed.

TABLE 6. TOTAL MINIMUM SQUARE FOOT LOADS FOR BEAM DESIGN

House	*Average height and half width, pounds*
One-story........	50
Two-story.......	150
Three-story......	180

4. Determine the load per lineal foot on the beam. Assuming that Figure 31 is a two-story house, the total floor load would be arrived at by multiplying 150 lb. by the "half width," or 9 ft., which would give us 1,350 lb. It should be observed that the foregoing calculations for the load on the beam take into consideration the weight of the first floor, the second floor, and the attic ceiling, together with live loads of 30 lb. for each.

5. Compute the total load on the beam. Before it is possible to determine the exact size of beam to be used, it will be necessary to know the total load to be carried by the beam. If the load on the beam in Figure 31 is 1,350 lb. for each foot of length, the total load which it must carry per span of 8 ft. would be 8 times 1,350 lb., or 10,800 lb.

6. Select the material for the beam. If wood is to be used, it should be decided whether to use a built-up beam or a solid beam. Available materials sometimes decide this. Moreover, either will be satisfactory if properly made and installed.

7. Determine the size of the beam. When the total load on the beam has been computed and the type of beam to be used has been selected, there remains only the choice of the size. In Figure 31 the total beam load on an 8-ft. span was found to be 10,800 lb. Therefore, if we are using a solid-wood beam, we may refer to Table 7 and find that for an 8-ft. span carrying a load of 10,800 lb., the

TABLE 7. SAFE LOADS IN POUNDS FOR SOLID AND BUILT-UP WOOD BEAMS *

Size, inches	Spans				
	6 ft.	7 ft.	8 ft.	9 ft.	10 ft.
6 × 8 solid.........	6,874	5,891	5,148	4,584	4,124
6 × 8 built up......	6,090	4,220	4,560	4,062	3,654
6 × 10 solid........	11,029	9,451	8,260	7,355	6,618
6 × 10 built up.....	9,774	8,376	7,320	6,519	5,865
8 × 8 solid.........	9,373	8,033	7,020	6,251	5,624
8 × 8 built up......	8,120	6,960	6,080	5,416	4,872
8 × 10 solid........	15,038	12,887	11,262	10,027	9,023
8 × 10 built up.....	13,032	11,168	9,760	8,692	7,820

* Weyerhaeuser Forest Products, Saint Paul, Minn.

nearest figure to and over 10,800 lb. is the figure 11,262. Thus, following this line to the left to the column indicating the sizes, we find we would need to use a solid beam of the size 8 by 10 in.

Construction of wood beams. Almost all built-up wood beams are built on the job. Sometimes these are constructed first and then

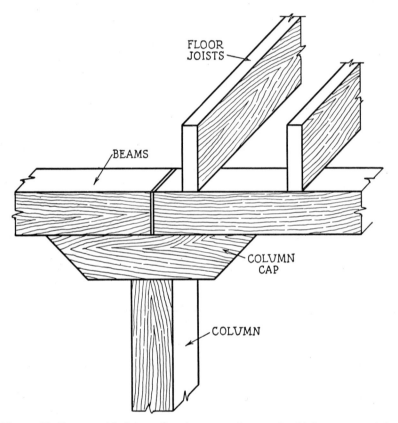

FLOOR
JOISTS

BEAMS

COLUMN
CAP

COLUMN

Figure 32. Beams with joints directly over columns should be supported by column caps installed at the top of the column.

raised into place and at other times they are built into place, one piece at a time. Built-up beams for the average construction are generally made up from three pieces of 2 by 8's or three pieces of 2 by 10's spiked together with 16*d* or 20*d* common nails. The nails should be spaced not farther apart than 18 in. and they should be well staggered toward the top and the bottom (Figure 29).

The ends of the solid and the built-up beams are supported by the columns. Each of these columns usually has a cap, as shown in Figure 32. The cap is spiked to the column with 16d common nails, and the beam is spiked to the cap in the same way by toenailing. The cap is made of solid material of the same size as the beam and

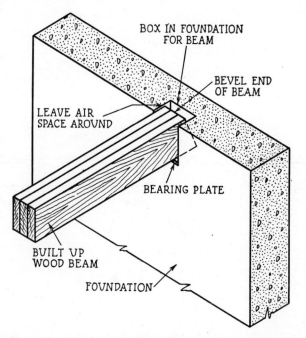

Figure 33. The ends of the beam at the wall rest on the wall foundation. They may be set into a pocket and should have not less than 4 in. of bearing surface.

the column, and it should be as long as three to four times the width of the column. The ends of the beam at the wall rest on the wall foundation. They may be set into a pocket of the wall, with not less than 4 in. of bearing, or they may be partly supported by a pilaster (Figure 33).

Construction for steel beams. If a steel beam is to be used, the method of ascertaining the size is practically the same as that used for wood beams. Referring to Figure 31 again, we find the total weight on the 8-ft. span to be 10,800 lb. Thus, by referring to Table 8, we locate the span in feet in the first column to the left. By follow-

TABLE 8. ALLOWABLE UNIFORM LOAD ON STEEL I BEAMS
IN THOUSANDS OF POUNDS *

Maximum Bending Stress: 16,000 lb. per sq. in.

Span, feet	*Depth and weight of sections*								
	10 *in.*		9 *in.*		8 *in.*		7 *in.*	6 *in.*	5 *in.*	4 *in.*
	40 *lb.*	25.4 *lb.*	35 *lb.*	21.8 *lb.*	25.5 *lb.*	18.4 *lb.*	15.3 *lb.*	12.5 *lb.*	10 *lb.*	7.7 *lb.*
2	149.8		131.8		86.6			27.6	21.0	15.2
3	112.8		88.3	52.2	60.8	43.2	35.0	25.8	17.2	10.6
4	84.6	62.0	66.2	50.3	45.6	37.9	27.6	19.4	12.9	8.0
5	67.7	52.1	53.0	40.3	36.5	30.3	22.1	15.5	10.3	6.4
6	56.4	43.4	44.2	33.6	30.4	25.3	18.4	12.9	8.6	5.3
7	48.4	37.2	37.9	28.8	26.1	21.7	15.8	11.1	7.4	4.5
8	42.3	32.6	33.1	25.2	22.8	19.0	13.8	9.7	6.4	4.0
9	37.6	28.9	29.4	22.4	20.3	16.9	12.3	8.6	5.7	3.5
10	33.9	26.0	26.5	20.1	18.2	15.2	11.0	7.7	5.2	3.2
11	30.8	23.7	24.1	18.3	16.6	13.8	10.0	7.0	4.7	
12	28.2	21.7	22.1	16.8	15.2	12.6	9.2	6.5	4.3	
13	26.0	20.0	20.4	15.5	14.0	11.7	8.5	6.0		
14	24.2	18.6	18.9	14.4	13.0	10.8	7.9	5.5		
15	22.6	17.4	17.7	13.4	12.2	10.1	7.4			
16	21.2	16.3	16.6	12.6	11.4	9.5	6.9			

* Loads above upper horizontal lines will produce maximum allowable shear in webs. Loads below lower horizontal lines will produce excessive deflections.

ing this line across the table to the nearest figure in pounds over the required weight of 10,800 lb., we find the figure 13.8. This means 13,800 lb. Thus, by following up the column from this figure to the top of the table, we find the size of beam that is needed to be a 7-in., 15.3-lb. steel I beam. The length of course would equal the span in feet, or 8 ft. The beam required then would be (for each span),

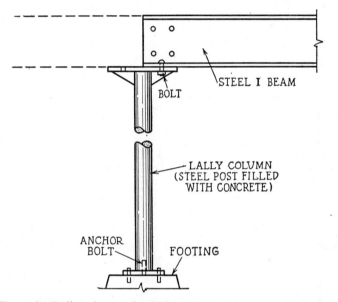

Figure 34. Lally columns should be bolted to the beams at the top.

one 7-in., 15.3-lb. steel I beam, 8 ft. long. Steel beams are usually installed with Lally columns as supports. Such columns are made of cylindrical steel pipe, which is filled with a mix of portland-cement concrete (Figure 34). However, steel beams installed over wood columns are very satisfactory (Figure 15).

FLOOR JOISTS

Definition. Joists may be either floor joists or ceiling joists. They are those members of the frame that actually carry the subflooring. Their ends may be supported by the beams and by the foundation walls (Figure 35). If used in a two-story house, they may be both floor joists and ceiling joists by forming a ceiling for the down-stairs and a floor for the upstairs. However, joists that have flooring nailed onto one side that forms a floor are usually called "floor joists," regardless of where they are used.

Purpose. Their purpose is to provide a suitable structure onto which the habitable floors of the house may be built.

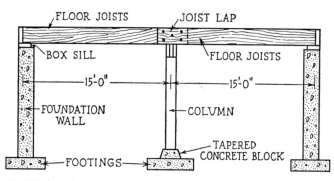

Figure 35. With a floor joist span of 15 ft., the lumber length needed would be 16 ft. The extra length would be used for the lap in the middle.

Spacing. Floor joists are generally spaced 16 in. on center. They may be spaced otherwise at times, but joists spaced farther apart would need to be larger and would probably be more costly in con-struction. Sometimes it is necessary to place floor joists as close together as 12 in., in order for them to carry the weight placed upon them without having their size increased. As most plaster lath is made in lengths of 48 in. and less, it is advisable to space the joists 16 in. apart. Spacing should be started at one side of the house and continued entirely across the house. Under all partitions, extra joists should be inserted between the regularly spaced joists to carry the added weight.

Size of joists. The size of floor joists is determined in much the same manner as that for beams. It must be decided just how much weight will be placed on each joist, and when this is known, ref-erence to Table 9 will give the correct size of timber to be used. For example, the joists in Figure 35 have a span of 15 ft., spaced 16 in.

on center. If the load (live and dead) be 50 lb. per sq. ft., which is average for one-story houses, the procedure would be as follows: 16 in., or 1⅓ ft., times 15 ft. times 50 lb., or

$$1\frac{1}{3} \times 15 \times 50 = 1,000 \text{ lb.}$$

Thus, by referring to Table 9 and locating the figure 15, which represents the span, then following down that column of figures to the

TABLE 9. FLOOR JOISTS *

Allowable fiber stress 1,200 lb. per sq. in. for southern pine or Douglas fir. Allowable uniformly distributed loads for joists and beams in pounds computed for actual dressed sizes.

Solid dressed sizes, in.	Spans, feet										
	8	9	10	11	12	13	14	15	16	17	18
2 × 6	837	738	660	595	541	494	454	419	388	360	335
2 × 8	1,503	1,331	1,191	1,075	980	898	827	766	712	662	619
2 × 10	2,020	2,020	1,912	1,730	1,578	1,449	1,336	1,238	1,153	1,077	1,009
2 × 12	2,435	2,435	2,435	2,435	2,328	2,136	1,973	1,832	1,708	1,597	1,497
2 × 14	3,065	3,065	3,065	3,065	3,065	3,065	2,729	2,534	2,366	2,212	2,076

*Loads given on the right of the heavy zigzag line will cause a deflection greater than ⅟₃₆₀ of the span. Loads given on the left of the line will cause a deflection less than ⅟₃₆₀ of the span.

nearest and over 1,000 lb., we find 1,238. By following this line to the left to the first column, we find indicated that a 2- by 10-in. timber would be needed.

Tables have also been prepared for finding the size of floor joists when only the span and the load per square foot are known. For example, in Table 10, if we were to use the joists, spans, and spacings as indicated in Figure 35, with no plastered ceiling, we would refer to the first line in the table indicating the live load with or without a plastered ceiling, in this case 50 lb. Then by following this column

TABLE 10. JOISTS SPANS

Span calculations provide for carrying the live loads shown and the additional weight of the joists and double flooring.

Size	Spacing	Live load, pounds							
		30		40		50		60	
		With plaster	None	With plaster	None	With plaster	None	With plaster	None
2″ × 6″	12″	11′ 6″	13′ 4″	10′ 8″	12′ 0″	10′ 0″	10′ 11″	9′ 6″	10′ 1″
	16″	10′ 6″	11′ 11″	9′ 9″	10′ 6″	9′ 1″	9′ 6″	8′ 7″	8′ 9″
	24″	9′ 3″	9′ 6″	8′ 6″	8′ 7″	7′ 10″	7′ 10″	7′ 2″	7′ 2″
2″ × 8″	12″	15′ 3″	17′ 9″	14′ 1″	15′ 10″	13′ 3″	14′ 5″	12′ 7″	13′ 4″
	16″	13′ 11″	15′ 5″	12′ 11″	13′ 10″	12′ 1″	12′ 7″	11′ 5″	11′ 8″
	24″	12′ 3″	12′ 5″	11′ 4″	11′ 5″	10′ 4″	10′ 4″	9′ 7″	9′ 7″
2″ × 10″	12″	19′ 2″	22′ 2″	17′ 9″	19′ 11″	16′ 8″	18′ 2″	15′ 10″	16′ 10″
	16″	17′ 6″	19′ 5″	16′ 3″	17′ 5″	15′ 3″	15′ 10″	14′ 6″	14′ 8″
	24″	15′ 6″	16′ 0″	14′ 3″	14′ 5″	13′ 1″	13′ 1″	12′ 1″	12′ 1″
2″ × 12″	12″	23′ 0″	26′ 7″	21′ 4″	23′ 11″	20′ 1″	21′ 10″	19′ 1″	20′ 2″
	16″	21′ 1″	23′ 7″	19′ 7″	21′ 0″	18′ 5″	19′ 1″	17′ 5″	17′ 8″
	24″	18′ 8″	19′ 3″	17′ 3″	17′ 4″	15′ 9″	15′ 9″	14′ 7″	14′ 7″

down until we came to a figure nearest and over that representing our span, we would find it to be 15 ft. 10 in. Then by following this line to the left, we would find indicated in the first column that a 2- by 10-in. timber would be needed.

Construction. In the placing and nailing of floor joists, consideration must be given to the type of framing to be used. Nailing will be different in braced framing from that in western framing. Joists should always be nailed to the sills whenever possible and to the beams. The 16d common nails are usually large enough, but occasionally it is necessary to use 20d commons. The joists should be cut long enough to provide a bearing on each end of at least 4 in. Square one end of the joist and, if a lapped joist is being used, it is not necessary to square the lapped end. Joists lapped on top of the beam are considered very good construction (Figure 36). However, this method reduces headroom.

When headroom is reduced, this requires a higher foundation and adds to the cost of the house. This type is also used a great deal in

Figure 36. Joists lapped on top of the girder. A very good method but it reduces headroom. When headroom is reduced it requires a higher foundation wall. This, of course, adds to the cost of the house.

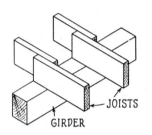

Figure 37. Girder construction for balloon framing. The joists are notched out and rest on a ledger strip. This method does not reduce the headroom in the basement.

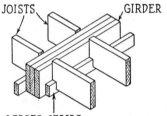

Figure 38. This is a girder construction for braced and western framing.

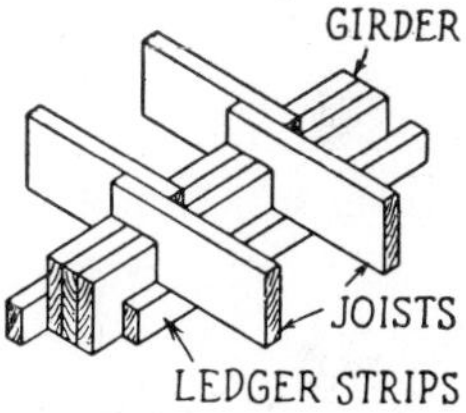

basementless houses where only crawl spaces are left. Joist construction for balloon framing is shown in Figure 37. Ledger strips must be used and well-fitted joints must be secured. This method increases the headroom in the basement.

A joist-and-beam assembly, used largely in western or platform framing, is shown in Figure 38. Joists installed in brick or masonry walls should have their ends at the wall cut at an angle (Figure 39) for self-releasing in case of fire. If the joists burned through and

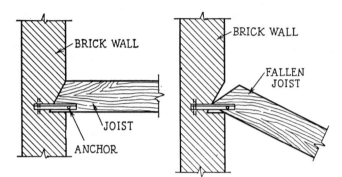

Figure 39. Joists installed in masonry walls should have the ends cut at an angle for self-releasing in case of fire.

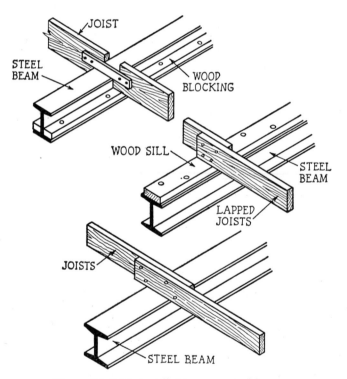

Figure 40. Joists installed in or on steel beams.

fell, they should fall free of the masonry wall; otherwise, they would probably tear out the wall severely. Floor joists in masonry walls should be anchored to the walls about every 4 to 6 ft. This ties the walls to the building and prevents bulging or spreading. These ties are usually T-shaped irons bolted to the sides of the joists. Ties are often used also at right angles to the joists, about every 6 ft. apart. This should be done with long straps extending through three or four joists. Joists installed in or on steel beams are constructed in much the same manner as for wood beams. Examples of this construction are shown in Figure 40.

JOIST HEADERS

Definition. Joist headers are auxiliary joists, usually run at right angles to the regular joists.

Purpose. They are used wherever it is necessary to cut regular joists in order to provide an opening, such as a stair well, a hearth

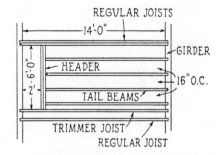

Figure 41. Joist headers are used where it is nesessary to cut regular joists to provide an opening.

well, or a chimney. They are spiked to the ends of the joists that have been cut (Figure 41).

Size. Although the size of joist headers is usually the same as that of joists, it is sometimes necessary to double the header in order to carry the load.

Spacing. Spacing is determined by the size of the opening made in the floor or the ceiling. The length of the header is the distance between its two supports. The header should fit tightly between the trimmers and should be well spiked through the trimmer into the ends of the header.

Construction.   Regardless of their length, headers for joists are generally doubled. Sometimes this is not necessary and sometimes it is not sufficient to carry the load. When a double header is not sufficient to carry the load, columns should be used and the headers figured for size on the same basis as for girders or beams. Loads imposed at the ends of joist headers are usually great compared to other joist assemblies. Therefore, nailing is very important. Spike through the trimmer into the single header using 20d common nails. Then spike in through the header into the ends of all the tail beams. Then install the second or double header and spike it onto the first header with 20d common nails. If a double trimmer is used, it should be installed next and spiked onto the first trimmer and the headers with 20d common nails.

TRIMMERS

Definition.   Any regular or extra joist supporting a header is called a "trimmer" (Figure 41).

Purpose.   Trimmers are used to support the headers.

Size.   Their size is the same as that of joists.

Construction.   For the construction of trimmers, see directions for joists.

CEILING JOISTS

Definition.   Ceiling joists are those members of the frame that carry the plaster and form the ceiling of the room. They should be large enough and strong enough to form a rigid construction that will be free from bending or buckling, thus preventing plaster's cracking. As a rule they carry no live load unless attic storage space is provided. In this case, a live load of 20 lb. per sq. ft. of floor space should be taken into account when figuring for their size, and bridging should be used. If there are rooms in the attic, the joists should be considered the same as floor joists.

Purpose. Their purpose is to form a part of the frame of the building by tying the walls together at the top, tying the rafters together, and forming a construction onto which the lath and plaster may be applied (Figure 42).

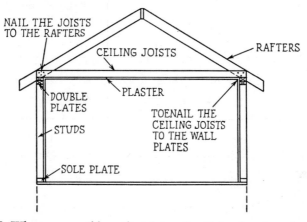

Figure 42. Whenever possible, ceiling joists should be placed so that they tie the building together at the top plate.

Size. Ceiling joists are generally installed 16 in. apart on centers. This allows standard-size lath to be used, which is 48 in. long. Spacing should start at one side of the house and should be carried all the way across the house from one side to the other. Space marks are usually made along the top of the double plates. If extra joists are needed for any purpose, they are dropped into place as extras and do not affect the original spacing order. The size of ceiling joists is determined the same way as that for floor joists, by the span and by the load to be carried (see Table 9).

The average weights to be used under average conditions for computing ceiling-joist sizes are shown in Table 11. For example, if a room has a ceiling-joist span of 13 ft. 11 in., with a plastered ceiling and an attic storage space, we should refer to Table 10.

For these requirements we find in Table 11 a floor load of 30 lb. per sq. ft. Again referring to Table 10, we find the joist span required listed under the 30 lb. per sq. ft. load, with spacing 16 in. on center;

TABLE 11. AVERAGE WEIGHTS IN POUNDS PER SQUARE FOOT OF LIVE
AND DEAD LOADS FOR CEILING JOISTS

Ceiling joists	Combined live and dead loads (average)
Ceiling with dead weight, plus plastered surface..................	20 lb. per sq. ft.
Attic floored, light storage only, plastered ceiling....................	20 lb. per sq. ft.
Attic floored with full storage rooms, walls, plastered ceiling...........	30 lb. per sq. ft.
Second floor, habitable rooms, plastered ceiling....................	40 lb. per sq. ft.

and by following this line across to the left, we find the size to be a 2- by 8-in. piece.

Construction.   Installation of ceiling joists is much the same as that for floor joists. The lengths are determined in the same way. The ceiling joists rest on the wall plates and are nailed to both the plates and the rafters, wherever possible. Ceiling joists should extend in one continuous line across the building and should be lapped and spiked together over the bearing partitions and should be located parallel with the rafters. Ceiling joists, like floor joists, should be installed with the crown or camber up.

Ceiling joists are often required to serve as both ceiling joists and rafters, as in flat-roof construction. This type of roof has wide acceptance in some localities. The joists are figured to carry the increased load of the roof, and in some cases they extend out over the walls to form an overhang (Figure 43). This type of extended joist

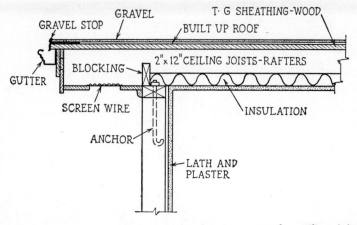

Figure 43. In modern architecture it is often necessary for ceiling joists to act also as rafters.

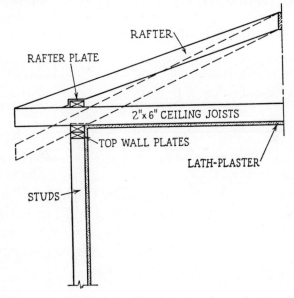

Figure 44. This type of extended ceiling joist may be used to increase the outside wall height of the building.

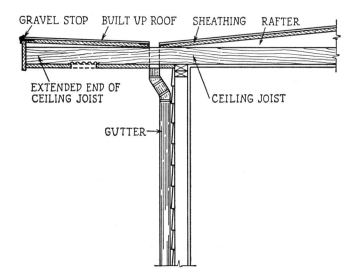

Figure 45. The ceiling jost may be extended to provide a wide overhang.

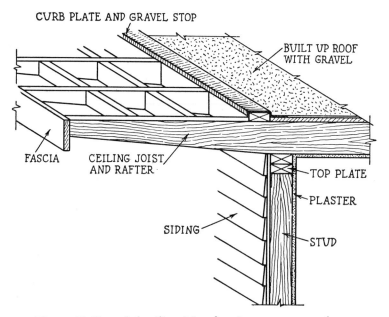

Figure 46. Extended ceiling joists forming an open overhang.

is also used to increase the wall height on the outside of the building when this is desired (Figure 44). Wide overhangs on buildings of both closed and open type are usually extended ceiling joists (Figure 45). A commonly used assembly for an open overhang, usually found on ranch-style architecture, is shown in Figure 46. These are merely ceiling joists extended.

HOW TO INSTALL BRIDGING

Definition. Bridging may be composed of short pieces of 1 by 2's, 1 by 3's, 1 by 4's, or 2 by 2's, cut and nailed in between the floor

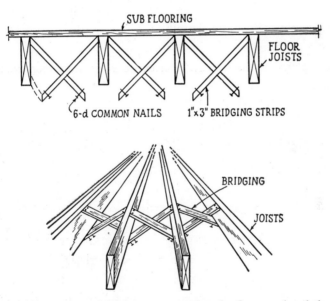

Figure 47. The purpose of bridging is to stiffen the floors and to help in distributing the loads more evenly. Bridging should be cut and nailed into place at the top only as soon as all joists are in place and before any flooring is nailed onto the joists.

joists to form a cross, or X, pattern (Figure 47). Practically any good grade of softwood is suitable. Bridging should be installed as soon as the joists are in and before any subflooring is nailed on.

Purpose. The purpose of bridging is to stiffen the floors and help in distributing the loads more evenly onto the joists. A load suddenly applied to a properly bridged floor joist is transmitted through the bridging to the neighboring joists and thus absorbed without damage.

Spacing. It is customary to insert rows of bridging every 5 to 8 ft. apart. If joists have a span of 10 ft., at least one row of bridging should be installed. If the spans are greater than this, two rows should be installed. However, joist spans greater than 16 to 18 ft. are seldom used. To be effective, they should be in straight lines or rows along the floor, so that each strut may abut directly opposite those adjacent to it.

Construction. Bridging should be cut and nailed into place at the top side only (Figure 47), just as soon as the joists are all in place and before any subflooring is applied. Leaving the lower ends loose until all the subflooring is nailed on is advisable because placing the subflooring will tend to bring the tops of all the joists into alignment. As soon as the subflooring is in place, the bridging should be nailed at the bottom. Some builders even prefer to wait until the finish floors have been installed.

HOW TO LAY SUBFLOORING

Definition. Subflooring is the first floor laid over the floor joists. Onto this subfloor is installed the finished flooring. The type of finished flooring to be used usually determines the type of subfloor needed. Subflooring may be any of the following materials:

1. Number 1 common yellow pine in square-edge material of uniform width such as $25/_{32}$ in. by 6-, 8-, 10-, and 12-in. widths, and in lengths of 2, 4, 6, 8, 10, 12 ft., etc.
2. Number 1 common yellow pine in edge-matched material usually $25/_{32}$ in. by 6 in. and tongued and grooved on the edges. Lengths are in multiples of 2 ft.

3. Number 1 common yellow pine or equal in end-matched or end- and edge-matched materials, usually $25/32$ in. by 6 in., and in lengths of 6, 8, 10, 12 ft., etc.

4. Douglas-fir plywood or equal in panels, $1/2$ in., $5/8$ in., $13/16$ in. thick, and 4, 8, 10, and 12 ft. in length.

Purpose. The purposes are manifold:

1. To provide a working floor
2. To strengthen construction
3. To provide a base for a finish floor
4. To provide additional deadening material
5. To increase insulation from the basement

Sizes. In frame-house construction, $13/16$ in. by 6 in.-, 8 in.-, or 10 in.-wide yellow pine is very popular. The lengths may vary as to availability and convenience. The use of square-edge or matched-edge material is a matter of choice. When plywood subflooring is to be used, it is necessary to know the type of finish flooring that will be used. In some cases a subfloor of $5/8$-in. plywood may be used and an underlayment of another $3/8$-in.-thick plywood used where finish floors are to be carpeted or are to receive asphalt tile, linoleum, etc.

How to lay. There are two generally used methods of laying subfloor:

1. The first is to place and nail the flooring squarely across the joists.

2. The other is to place and nail the flooring diagonally across the joists.

Of the two methods, it is more economical to lay the floor square across the joists because it takes less labor. It is easier to cut, takes less time, and wastes less material. It has one disadvantage, however, in that the finish floor can be laid only at right angles to it.

Diagonal subflooring is much more difficult to lay because each piece needs to have two diagonal cuts, one at each end. These, of course, are made over the joists and naturally cause a waste of material and a loss of time. However, a diagonally laid floor is considered stronger and also gives a choice of laying the finish floor in either direction. All subflooring should be nailed at every joist. Flooring up to 6 in. wide should be nailed on with two 8d common nails, and flooring up to 10 in. wide should be nailed on with three 8d common nails. All joints should be made directly over the joists unless end-matched material is being used.

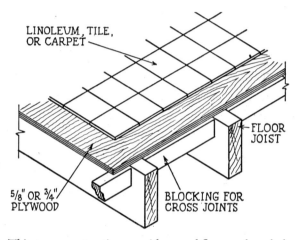

LINOLEUM, TILE, OR CARPET

FLOOR JOIST

5/8" OR 3/4" PLYWOOD

BLOCKING FOR CROSS JOINTS

Figure 48. This type construction provides a subfloor and underlay combination all in one.

Plywood sheets used for subflooring are generally nailed on at right angles to the floor joists. Plywood has great strength, both lengthwise and crosswise of the panel, because of its cross-lamination construction. As a result of this, plywood ⅝ in. thick will often do the work of plain boards much thicker. The most popular subflooring construction with plywood is that using ⅝-in. panels installed with outer plies of panels at right angles to the joists spaced 16 in. on center. When the finish floor is of $^{25}/_{32}$-in. hardwood or strip wood, no blocking is required between the joists at the panel joints. When the finish floor is less than $^{25}/_{32}$ in. or is of wood block, block parquetry, linoleum, composition, rubber, tile, etc., blocking is required under the panel edges at right angles to the joists.

All plywood subflooring should be nailed 6 in. on center at all edges and 10 to 12 in. on center at all intermediate members. All underlayment plywood is usually ⅜ in. thick. For all plywood panels ⅝ in. thick or over, up to and including ¾ in., use 8d common nails. For ½-in. plywood and less, use 6d common nails. Figure 48 shows the construction used when subflooring is of ¾-in. ply-

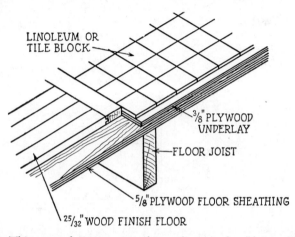

LINOLEUM OR
TILE BLOCK

⅜" PLYWOOD
UNDERLAY

FLOOR JOIST

⅝" PLYWOOD FLOOR SHEATHING

25/32" WOOD FINISH FLOOR

Figure 49. This type of construction shows the use of a ⅝ in. subfloor with a 25/32 in. finished wood floor and an underlayment of ⅜ in. plywood panel to bring the linoleum or tile up to the required height.

wood panels with all edges supported by cross-joint blocks. These blocks may be of 2- by 2- or 2- by 4-in. material. The ends should be well toenailed into the joists and the tops should be level and even with the tops of the joists. This installation may be used where the finish floor is to be wall-to-wall carpet, linoleum, tile block, etc. A 13/16-in. hardwood flooring could be used over this, but a thinner plywood panel could be used with equally good results (Figure 49). When 25/32-in. wood finish floors are used, a subfloor of ⅝ in. is sufficient.

When tile and linoleum floors are to match the height of the 25/32-in. wood floor, it is necessary to use an underlayment. This may be of ⅜-in. plywood panels. The construction shown in Figure 50 is used when the subfloor is of regular square- or matched-edge lumber, and an underlayment is needed for the installation of linoleum, tile, carpet, etc. Construction is shown in Figure 51, when ½-in. wood-block or -strip finish flooring is used. Here a ⅝-in. panel subfloor is sufficient, with the joists 16 in. on center. Again

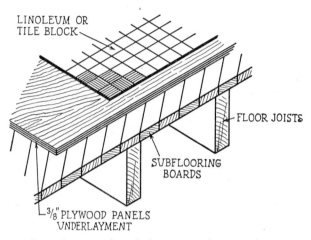

Figure 50. Where the use of underlayment only is used over regular subflooring, the subflooring may be 1 × 4 in., 1 × 6 in., 1 × 8 in., 1 × 10 in., etc.

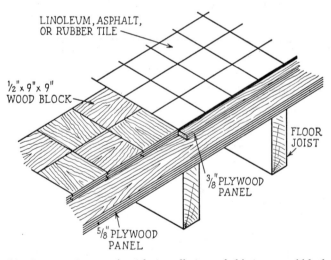

Figure 51. Construction used with installation of ½ in. wood-block finish floor, finishing even with tile, etc.

an underlayment of ⅜-in. plywood panel will be needed for tile, asphalt, carpet, linoleum, etc.

When all finish floor is to be the same thickness, a combination subfloor and underlayment makes a very good construction (Figure

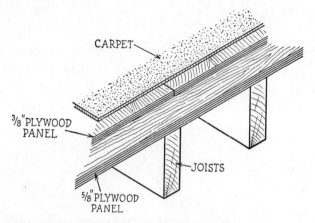

Figure 52. Combination of subfloor and underlayment. This may be used when the finish floor is all to be the same thickness.

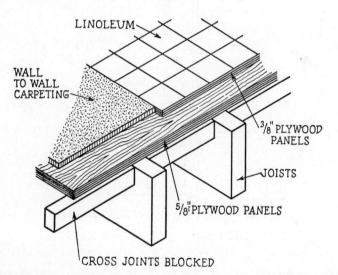

Figure 53. Carpet and linoleum combination over ⅝ in. plywood with an underlayment for the linoleum.

52). Construction used where the finish floor is to be carpeted is shown in Figure 53. If linoleum or composition floors are to be matched up, an underlayment will be needed of ⅜-in. plywood panel. All cross joints should be blocked as shown.

SOLE PLATES

Definition. Sole plates are horizontal members, usually 2- by 4-in. pieces, placed at the bottom of a frame wall or a stud partition (Figure 54).

Purpose. The purpose of sole plates is to carry the studs.

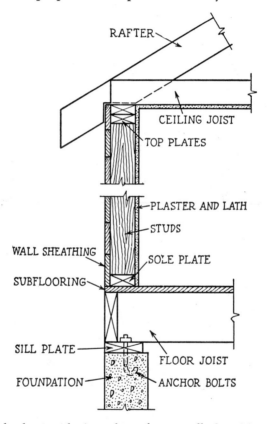

RAFTER

CEILING JOIST

TOP PLATES

PLASTER AND LATH

STUDS

WALL SHEATHING

SOLE PLATE

SUBFLOORING

SILL PLATE

FLOOR JOIST

FOUNDATION

ANCHOR BOLTS

Figure 54. Sole plates are horizontal members, usually 2 × 4 in. pieces, placed at the bottom of a frame wall or stud partitions.

Size. They are usually the same size and width as the studs.

Construction. Sole plates are used in platform framing under the stud walls, where the studs do not rest on walls or beams or do not pass through the floor to the sill plate below. Sole plates are usually nailed directly to the subflooring and into the box sill. They should

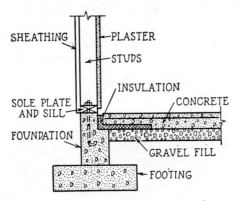

Figure 55. With concrete slab floors, the sole plate also acts as a sill plate.

be nailed down with 20*d* common nails. In cases of basementless houses, and especially over concrete slab floors, the sole plate acts also as a sill plate. It is bolted down to the concrete floor (Figure 55).

TOP PLATES

Definition. A top plate is the horizontal member found at the top of the partition or frame wall (Figure 56).

Purpose. Its purpose is to form a cap for the studs and also a plate or support for the ceiling joists and rafters. Sometimes it also serves as a support for other studs, either in gable ends or on second floors.

Size. The plates are always of the same material and size as the studs, except, of course, in length. Lengths may vary as requirements demand.

How to construct. It is customary to construct a double plate around the top of all walls and partitions. This provides a good bearing wall and also makes it possible to secure a good lap joint at corners and partition intersections. The plates should be spiked onto the ends of the studs with two 16d common nails. Each plate should be nailed on separately.

HOW TO BUILD STUD WALLS

Definition. Studs are the vertical members or pieces that go to make up the outside walls and all partitions. They are supported by the floor sole plate and, in turn, support the top plates (Figure 56).

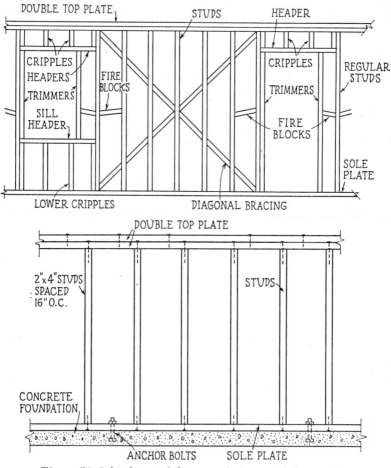

Figure 56. Sole plate and first top plate are nailed to studs.

Purpose. They form a definite part of the construction of the house, or framework. They support the weight of the upper part of the house or everything above the top-plate line. They form the framework to which is nailed the wall sheathing on the outside. On the inside they support the lath and plaster and insulation.

Size. Except in special cases or lengths greater than 14 ft., 2- by 4-in. studs will be strong enough. Most modern construction in platform framing will require 8-ft. studs per floor. The type of framing will determine the length of the studs.

Spacing. The standard spacing for studs is 16 in. This is to enable the use of lath that has a standard length of 4 ft. This is

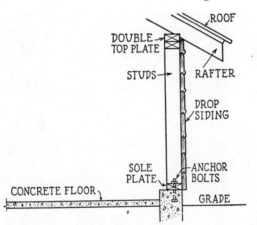

Figure 57. Summer cabins and smaller buildings may have siding nailed directly on the studs.

necessary in all construction designed to carry lath and plaster. However, there are some places where longer spacing is permissible, for example, in garages (Figure 57), summer cabins, etc., where other than plaster is used inside.

How to build stud walls. Usually, sections of stud walls are constructed at one time flat on the floor and then raised into place. This enables the builder to lay off and space them in an easy way. It also enables him to nail the floor plate and top plate on better by spiking through the plates into the ends of the studs. This method usually results in a better job because it avoids toenailing at the sole plate.

In selecting lumber for studs, choose straight uniform material, as it makes a wall that is more free from hollow places and bulges. After a wall is erected, take care to see that each section is well tied, or braced, and that it is plumb in all directions. After all walls are erected, the double top plate should be nailed in place.

HOW TO BUILD CORNER STUDS AND PARTITION STUDS

Definition. Studs used at the corner of a building or at the intersection of frame walls are usually built up from one or more ordinary studs. This is necessary to increase the strength at these points because of the added load found here. As an ordinary stud is generally a 2- by 4-in. piece of a given length, and strength, the strength can be multiplied by the number of pieces assembled. These built-up assemblies are called "corner posts" and "partition posts."

Size. The size of studs for all general frame-house construction is 2 by 4 in. Studs are generally spaced 16 in. on centers, depending on the type of construction used. Therefore, the sizes for corner posts and partition posts are the same as for regular studs, except as increased by building up.

Construction. Corner posts and partition posts are built first as a separate unit and then installed into the stud wall while it is still on

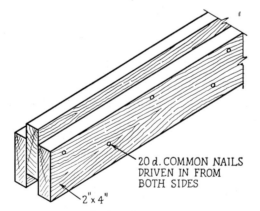

20 d. COMMON NAILS
DRIVEN IN FROM
BOTH SIDES

2" x 4"

Figure 58. Corner posts are spiked together before they are installed into the stud wall.

the floor, the same as any other stud (Figure 58). Several types of corner studs or posts and their methods of building up are shown in Figure 59. Figure 59*A* is perhaps the most simple and most satisfac-

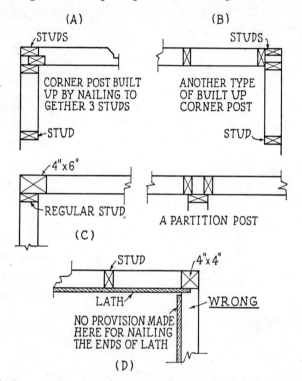

Figure 59. Corner posts or studs occur at the intersection of two walls at right angles with each other. They should be built so that the ends of all laths can be securely nailed to them.

tory in common use today. Type *B* does not provide so much surface for nailing the lath as type *A*. Types *C* and *D* are sometimes used, but both require materials special to ordinary construction.

WINDOW AND DOOR HEADERS

Definition. Wherever doors and windows occur, parts of the stud wall must be cut away. Thus it becomes necessary to install pieces called "headers" over the opening to support the lower ends

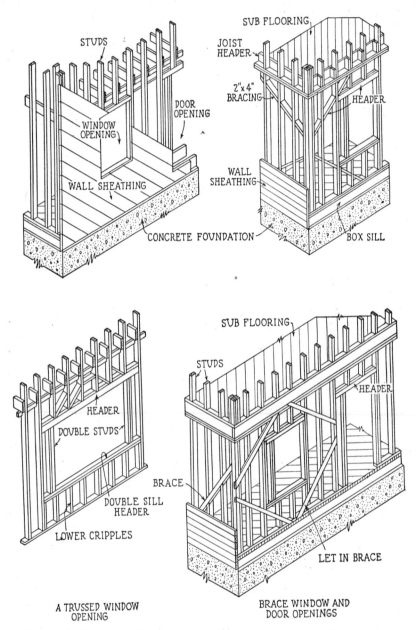

Figure 60. Typical wall constructions showing window and door headers.

of the studs that have been cut off (Figure 60). If it is a window, there will be a similar piece at the bottom called a "rough sill." This, of course, is to pick up the remaining pieces of studs that have not been cut out.

Purpose. The purpose is to support the studs that have been cut away and to construct a strong frame into which a doorjamb or window frame may be fitted.

Size. In order to determine the size of headers, first determine whether or not they are load-bearing or nonload-bearing. If they

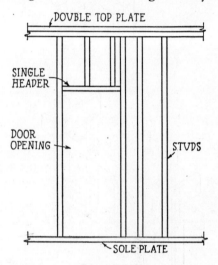

Figure 61. Openings that are non-load-bearing need not have double headers. These occur only in small openings. Regular studs are always placed 16 in. on center. Extra studs are used at the sides of all openings. Studs are spaced 16 in. O.C. in order to pick up lath.

are nonload-bearing and not more than 3 ft. wide, a single 2 by 4 will make a satisfactory header (Figure 61). However, inside trim is sometimes too wide to nail satisfactorily, and wider headers are needed for this purpose only.

If they are load-bearing walls, all the headers should be doubled and rest on studs, as shown in Figures 62 to 64. The 2 by 4's used for headers should be laid on edge vertically side by side with a piece of lath inserted between them to make them full 3⅝ in. thick, or the same as the stud.

Spacing. Be sure to allow sufficient space in the rough opening for doorjambs or window frames to be installed with ease and to be plumbed and leveled.

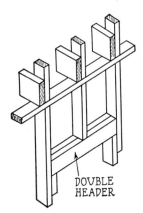

DOUBLE
HEADER

Figure 62. Openings that **are** load-bearing should always **be** double headed. If 2 by 4's are used on edge, spacers of lath or thin pieces of wood are used to make the header as thick as the studs.

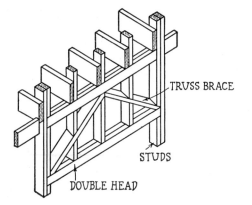

TRUSS BRACE

STUDS

DOUBLE HEAD

Figure 63. Openings that have extreme weight are to be trussed. This diverts the weight from the center to the outside at the studs.

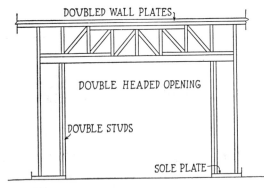

DOUBLED WALL PLATES

DOUBLE HEADED OPENING

DOUBLE STUDS

SOLE PLATE

Figure 64. For all openings of 3 ft. or more, the header will need to be trussed. There are several arrangements of trusses. This type is generally used over wide doors and group windows.

WHERE TO USE TRUSSES

Definition. Trusses are arrangements of framing material so constructed as to divert the weight at a given point to some other place.

Purpose. They are used over openings where doors or windows occur, to shift the weight to the sides of the openings and thus prevent sagging of the wall above and cracking of the plaster.

Sizes. For all openings of 3 ft. or over the header will need to be trussed. There are several arrangements of trusses. Figure 63 shows an arrangement widely used in the trade and very satisfactory. Figure 64 shows a truss arrangement over an opening 6 to 8 ft. wide. This type is generally used over wide doors and group windows.

BRACING

Definition. Bracing in frame-house construction may mean any method used to stiffen or make more rigid the frame against winds, storms, strain, or twist from any source. In some sections of the country this feature of building construction is very important. Good bracing also prevents plaster cracking, which of course is one of the results of undue stress or strain from some cause.

Construction. There are *three* generally used types of frame bracing considered to be very good. They are:

1. Cut-in bracing
2. Let-in bracing
3. Diagonally applied sheathing

Cut-in bracing (Figure 60) consists of 2 by 4's cut off at an angle and toenailed in between the studs. While this is good, it probably has the lowest strength value of the three here mentioned. Let-in bracing (Figure 60) consists of letting flush into the edge of the studs a 1- by 4- or a 1- by 6-in. piece at a diagonal from the top plates to the sole plates. These braces are then nailed to the studs with two 8*d* common nails at each joint. This method is considered to have a higher strength value than method 1. Perhaps the highest strength values are obtained by the use of wood sheathing applied diagonally to the wall (Figure 60). Each sheathing board in itself acts as a brace on the wall. However, if plywood sheathing ⅝ in. thick or more is used, a still greater strength can be obtained, and other methods of bracing may be omitted. Tests at the U.S. Forest Products Laboratory show that walls sheathed with plywood are twice as rigid and more than twice as strong as other constructions previously considered superior (see Wall Sheathing).

WALL SHEATHING

Definition.   Outside wall sheathing is used in much the same way as subflooring. It is nailed directly onto the framework of the house or studs. However, there is some wall sheathing that cannot be used satisfactorily as subflooring.

Purpose.   The purpose of wall sheathing is to strengthen the building by providing a base wall onto which the finish siding or wall can be nailed. It also provides an insulation in itself, and in some cases a base for further insulation.

Sizes and kinds.   There are many kinds of wall sheathing in use. Most widely used are the following:

1. Wood, $1\frac{3}{16}$ in. thick by 6, 8, 10, or 12 in. wide of No. 1 common square- or matched-edge material. It may be nailed on horizontally or diagonally.
2. Gypsum board, ½ in. thick by 24- and 48-in. widths and 8, 9, 10, and 12 ft. long.
3. Fiberboard, $2\frac{5}{32}$ in. thick by 24- and 48-in. widths and 8, 9, 10, and 12 ft. long.
4. Plywood, $\frac{5}{16}$ in., ⅜ in., ½ in., and ⅝ in. thick by 48 in. wide and 8, 9, 10, and 12 ft. long.

Construction.   Wood wall sheathing can be obtained in almost all widths, lengths, and grades. Generally used are widths from 6 to 12 in., with lengths selected for economical use. Almost all solid-wood wall sheathing used is $1\frac{3}{16}$ in. thick and either square or matched edge. This material may be nailed on horizontally or diagonally (Figure 65). By diagonal nailing, much greater strength is obtained. The material should be nailed on with three 8d common nails to each joint if the pieces are over 6 in. wide. Wood wall sheathing is laid on tight, with all joints made over the studs. If the sheathing is to be put on horizontally, it should be started at the

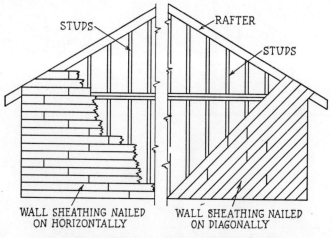

Figure 65. Nailing on solid-wood wall sheathing.

foundation and worked toward the top. If it is to be put on diagonally, it should be started at the corners of the building and worked toward the center or middle of the building.

Gypsum-board sheathing is made by casting a gypsum core within a heavy water-resistant fibrous envelope. The long edges of the 24-in. by 8-ft. boards are tongued and grooved. Each board is a full $\frac{1}{2}$ in. thick. Its use is mostly with wood siding that can be nailed directly through the sheathing and into the studs. It can also be used with brick-veneer construction when metal wall ties are fastened to the studs to hold the veneer, thus leaving the regulation 1-in. air space between the brick and the sheathing (Figure 66). Gypsum sheathing is fireproof, water resistant, windproof, does not warp nor absorb water, and does not require the use of building papers.

Fiberboard insulation sheathing is a structural insulating board manufactured with an "asphalt-coated" and "asphalt-impregnated" treatment. Fiberboard has received a very wide acceptance in the

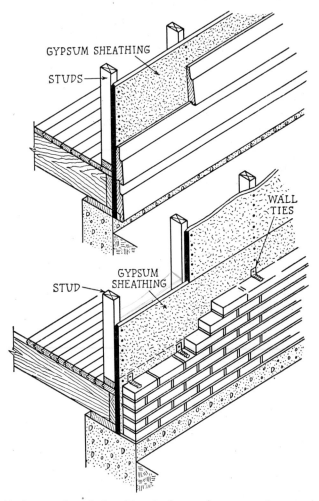

Figure 66. Gypsum-board sheathing is fireproof, water resistant, windproof, and does not require the use of building paper.

building industry and is probably being used as much or more than any other kind of wall sheathing. Reasons for this are many. For example, it is easy to handle, it covers large areas quickly, it has machined edges, it produces even and tight joints, it provides a rigid wall and has greater stiffening strength than ordinary horizontally applied wood boards. It also has high insulating values and is waterproof and windproof. The interlocking edges provide

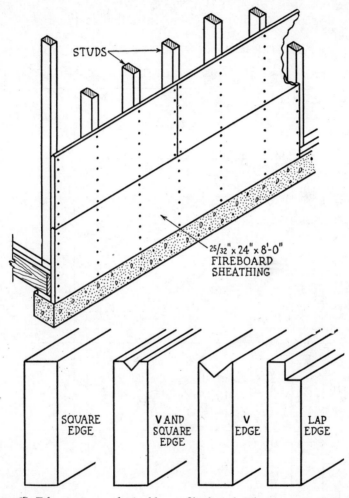

STUDS

$25/32'' \times 24'' \times 8'$-0''
FIREBOARD
SHEATHING

SQUARE
EDGE

V AND
SQUARE
EDGE

V
EDGE

LAP
EDGE

Figure 67. Edge patterns obtainable on fiberboard. These permit tight joints to be made.

some of these features and, of course, no building paper is needed or required. Fiberboard sheathing is usually applied horizontally by nailing it directly onto the studs. The nails should be 2 in. long for $25/32$-in. material and spaced about 4 in. on center (Figure 67).

Plywood as a wall sheathing has also gained wide favor among builders. Probable reasons for this could be attributed to the following factors: size, weight, stability, and structural properties, plus laborsaving costs in application. The rigidity chart (Table 12) shows that plywood imparts more than double the rigidity and

TABLE 12. STRENGTH AND RIGIDITY OF FRAME WALLS*

From U.S. Forest Products Laboratory Tests, Wall with Openings

Sheathing material	Relative rigidity	Relative strength
1″ × 8″ diagonally applied wood board sheathing............	1.0	1.3
2%2″ fiberboard, 8d nails spaced 3″ at all vertical edges, 5½″ to 6″ elsewhere............	1.6	2.1
1″ × 8″ horizontally applied wood board sheathing with 1″ by 4″ let in braces, two 8d nails per stud..................	1.5	2.2
¼″ plywood nailed. 6d nails spaced 5″ apart at edges, 10″ elsewhere..................	2.0	2.8

*Two fundamental properties of plywoods that establish them as excellent material for sheathing are (1) the cross laminations of the plies and (2) the large panel sizes. The weakest walls are those with openings. Without the openings, the wall would still possess greater strength. (Douglas Fir Plywood Association.)

strength of diagonally applied wood boards. As the result of this, when plywood sheathing is used, corner bracing is usually omitted. With plywood construction, this omission is also permitted in meeting the requirements of the F.H.A. Large-size panels effect a major

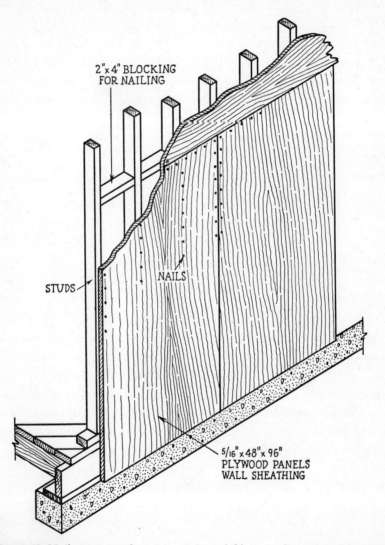

Figure 68. Nail not more than 6 in. O.C. and ⅜ in. in from the edge 12 in. other than along the edges.

saving in the time required for application, with a resulting saving in labor costs. Plywood also ensures a tight, draft-free installation and contributes a high insulation value to the wall.

Plywood, like any wood, possesses excellent insulating properties. It has the same coefficient of heat transmission as Douglas fir, that is, 0.78 B.t.u. per in. Minimum thicknesses of plywood wall sheathing are ⁵⁄₁₆ in. for 16-in. stud spacing and ⅜ in. for 24-in. stud spacing. The panels should be installed with the face grain parallel to the studs. However, a little more stiffness can be gained by installing them across the studs, but this requires more cutting and fitting.

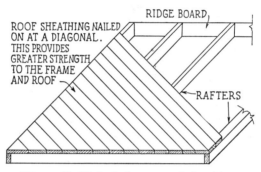

RIDGE BOARD

ROOF SHEATHING NAILED ON AT A DIAGONAL. THIS PROVIDES GREATER STRENGTH TO THE FRAME AND ROOF

RAFTERS

Figure 69. Tight-deck-type roof sheathing.

Use 6d common nails for ⁵⁄₁₆-, ⅜-, and ½-in. panels and 8d common nails for ⅝- and 1³⁄₁₆-in. panels. Space the nails not more than 6 in. on center at the edges of the panels and not more than 12 in. on center elsewhere. Standard construction uses the conventional lumber frame and U.S. Commercial Standard grades of plywood sheathing manufactured for covering floors, walls, and roofs. This is available at most local lumberyards. Methods of standard construction are shown in Figure 68.

ROOF SHEATHING

Definition. Roof sheathing is the term applied to that material or the boards that are nailed directly to the rafters.

Purpose. The purpose of roof sheathing is to provide a subsurface on which to nail shingles or the finished roof. It ties together the rafters, stiffens the building, and acts largely in the same capacity that subflooring and subsiding do. It also provides a certain amount of insulation, especially in the solid or tight-deck type (Figure 69).

Size. Sizes for tight deck will be the same as for subflooring and subsiding. Where wood shingles are used, strips for sheathing are generally used also. These strips vary in size from 1 by 3 to 1 by 4 to 1 by 6.

Spacing. It is necessary, however, in using these to space them as far apart on centers as the shingle is laid to the weather (Figure 70).

Figure 70. Roof sheathing is the term applied to the material or boards that are nailed directly on the rafters. Its purpose is to provide a subsurface on which to nail the shingles or the finished roof. Space the boards as far apart on centers as the shingle is laid to the weather.

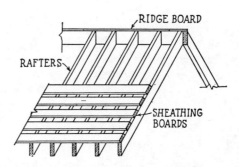

How to apply. In starting to put on sheathing one should start at the eaves with one good-quality wide board. The boards should be nailed at every rafter with two 8d common nails; if sheathing boards are over 6 in. wide, they should be secured with three nails each.

Generally speaking, the same materials may be used in roof sheathing that are acceptable in floor sheathing or subflooring. Plywood has many advantages over the solid-wood boards; however, there are some disadvantages. While the large panels have a tendency to cover the surface more quickly, they are also more difficult to handle and fit into valleys, around dormers, and onto cut-up roofs. They do provide added strength to the roof. Plywood is resistant to swelling and shrinking. It holds nails well, and in general provides a superior base for roofing materials.

Plywood sheathing should be nailed on with the grain of the face plies across the rafters. The nails should not be placed more

than 6 in. apart along the edges and not more than 10 to 12 in. apart
elsewhere. Panels ⅜ in., ½ in., and ⅝ in. thick in unsanded commercial grades are used, depending on the load to be carried and the
spacing of the rafters. Table 13 gives the recommended thicknesses

TABLE 13. RECOMMENDED THICKNESS FOR PLYSCORD (PLYWOOD) ROOF SHEATHING

Panels installed lengthwise across the rafters.

Roof load,* pounds per square foot	Rafter spacing, inches	Thickness, inches
20	18	⁵⁄₁₆
	22	⅜
	27	½
	33	⅝
40	12	⁵⁄₁₆
	16	⅜
	21	½
	24	⅝

* For deflection limited to ⅟₃₆₀ of span. (Douglas Fir Plywood Association.)

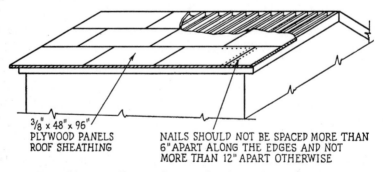

Figure 71. Installation of 4 × 8 ft. plywood roof sheathing.

for plywood roof sheathing. Sheathing less than ½ in. thick is not recommended where wood shingles are to be used. Installation of 4- by 8-ft. plywood roof sheathing is shown in Figure 71.

BUILDING PAPERS

Definition. Building paper is a special strong, heavy, waterproof paper used to nail on subfloors between the subfloor and the finish

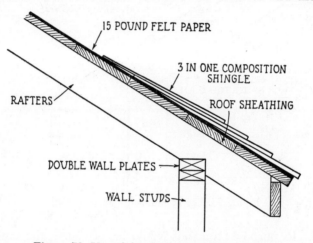

Figure 72. Use of felt building paper on roof.

floor. It is used to nail on wall sheathing between the sheathing and the finished outside walls, such as weatherboarding, wall shingles, and brick veneer. It is used to nail on the roof sheathing between the sheathing and the finish roof (Figure 72).

Where to use. Its use in all places is about the same. If properly applied, it prevents wind and air filtration.

Floors. On floors building paper prevents air and dust from the basement from sifting into the house through cracks. It also prevents moisture from the basement or any other source from entering the finish floor by absorption and thus guards against the swelling or buckling of the floors that would naturally result from this action. It also has some insulating value and sound-deadening effect, but not a great deal, as it is too thin.

Walls. Of course the same principles apply to the outside walls of a building as to the floor. The principal purpose of building paper is to prevent air, wind, dust, and moisture penetration from the outside (Figure 73).

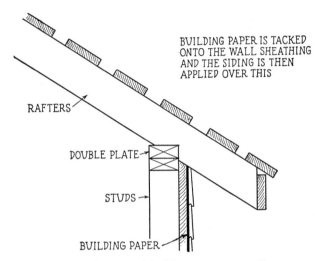

BUILDING PAPER IS TACKED ONTO THE WALL SHEATHING AND THE SIDING IS THEN APPLIED OVER THIS

RAFTERS

DOUBLE PLATE

STUDS

BUILDING PAPER

Figure 73. Use of building paper on wall.

Roof. Its purpose on a roof would be, of course, the same as on the floors and side walls. It adds, in this case, a double protection against leakage.

Size. Building paper comes in rolls usually from 200 to 500 sq. ft. in area. Weights will vary from 20 up to 75 lb. per square (a square equals a surface 10 ft. square, or 100 sq. ft.). Thus, if a roll of paper was listed as a 500-ft. roll of 20-lb. weight, it would indicate that the roll contained 5 squares of paper and would weigh 100 lb. Table 14 indicates how average papers are listed and sold.

Spacing. When applied to a building, all papers should have a sufficient lap, which should never be less than 3 in. Sometimes it is as much as half the width of the paper.

How to apply. Smooth out the paper to prevent bulges, humps, and bad joints. It is generally nailed on with common galvanized roof nails or with nails that have been supplied by the manufacturer. It is usually a good policy to follow the manufacturer's directions in applying building paper.

TABLE 14. BUILDING PAPERS

Kind	Description	Square feet	Weight, pounds
Slater's felt.......	Used under slate or tile	500	30
Red rosin paper...	Used over sheathing	500	20
Red rosin paper...	Used over sheathing	500	30
Red rosin paper...	Used over sheathing	500	40
Black insulating...	Waterproofed, used over sheathing	250	15
Black insulating...	Waterproofed, used over sheathing	500	30
Black insulating...	Waterproofed, used over sheathing	500	45
Deadening felt....	Used under floors and linoleum	450	60
Deadening felt....	Used under floors and linoleum	500	75
Duplex sheathing..	Double sheets cemented with asphalt	500	20
Roof sheathing....	Used under all kinds of shingles	200	50

2

RAFTER FRAMING

Rafters are those members of a roof that extend from the plate to the ridge or any part thereof. They serve the same purpose for the roof as the floor joists do for the floors (Figure 74), that is, to form a framework or construction that will provide a support for the roof sheathing and roofing material.

The size of a rafter usually depends upon the following:

1. The span
2. Kind of roof material to be used
3. Wind
4. Snow
5. Type of architecture

Maximum spans for wood rafters are given in Table 15. Spacings of rafters from 16 to 24 in. are common in small frame construction. Sometimes 20 in. is used, but with the use of 1-in. sheathing this is not always advisable, as the sheathing becomes too flexible at this distance. Plastering directly to the rafters from under is seldom done; however, if desired, the rafters should be spaced 16 in. on center.

Every effort should be made to reduce all outward thrust. If rafters are spaced the same as ceiling joists, they can be spiked together at the plate (Figure 75).

TABLE 15. MAXIMUM CLEAR SPANS OF RAFTERS FOR ROOFS WITH A MINIMUM SLOPE OF 5 TO 12

For wood and asphalt shingle roofs

Assumed total live and dead load, 40 lb. per sq. ft.

Nominal lumber size	Actual lumber size	Spacing center to center	Maximum clear span *		
			Minimum fiber stress, 1,200 lb.	Minimum fiber stress, 1,000 lb.	Minimum fiber stress, 1,000 lb.
			Douglas fir (coast region and Inland Empire) southern yellow pine, western larch	West coast hemlock, cypress, redwood, tamarack	All other softwoods
2″ × 4″	1⅝″ × 3⅝″	24″	6′ 6″	6′ 1″	5′ 1″
		20″	7′ 3″	6′ 7″	5′ 6″
		16″	8′ 1″	7′ 4″	6′ 2″
		12″	9′ 4″	8′ 6″	7′ 2″
2″ × 6″	1⅝″ × 5⅝″	24″	10′ 3″	9′ 4″	7′ 8″
		20″	11′ 4″	10′ 5″	8′ 8″
		16″	12′ 6″	11′ 5″	9′ 6″
		12″	14′ 2″	13′ 1″	11′ 0″
2″ × 8″	1⅝″ × 7½″	24″	13′ 8″	12′ 6″	10′ 0″
		20″	15′ 2″	13′ 8″	11′ 0″
		16″	16′ 7″	15′ 3″	12′ 1″
		12″	18′ 4″	16′ 7″	14′ 3″

Notes: Rafters for slate, tile, or asbestos-cement (rigid) shingle roofs must be of sufficient size to carry the load.

Where the allowable fiber stress of the species of wood used is in excess of 1,200 lb., increased spans will be permitted, provided they are determined on the same basis as those used for this table.

Rafters on roofs with slopes less than 5 to 12 should be figured the same as floor joists.

* The distance measured horizontally from the plate to a point directly beneath the ridge. The actual rafter length will depend upon the roof slope and must be determined accordingly.

It is always desirable to use a ridgeboard, which helps in the erection and alignment of the rafters (Figure 75).

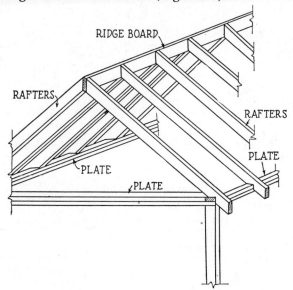

Figure 74. The purpose of rafters is to form a framework or construction that will provide a support for the roof sheathing and roofing.

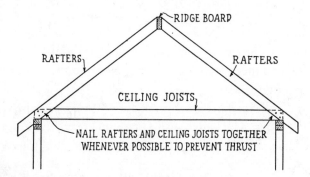

Figure 75. Spiking rafters and ceiling joists together at the plate.

The rafters should be notched over the plate and have a plate bearing of not less than 3 in. (Figure 76). Care should be taken at all times to maintain a level ridge. Whenever possible, collar beams should be employed to reduce span and rafter thrust.

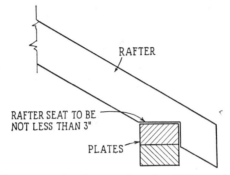

RAFTER

RAFTER SEAT TO BE
NOT LESS THAN 3"

PLATES

Figure 76. Rafter seat or bearing on plate should be not less than 3 in.

TYPES OF ROOFS

The most usual types of roof construction are as follows:

Gable roof. This is the most commonly used type. It has two roof slopes meeting at the center or ridge to form a gable. It is a good roof, usually trouble-free and easy to construct (Figure 77).

Lean-to or shed type. This type with only one slope is usually built next to or against another building. It is one of the least expensive roofs to build and is generally found in cheap construction (Figure 78).

Hip roof. This type of roof consists of four sides or slopes, all running toward the center of the building. Rafters at the corner run up diagonally to meet at the center or ridge. Into them other rafters are framed (Figure 79).

Gable and valley. This is a combination of two gable roofs intersecting each other. The valley is the place where the two meet, each roof, of course, slanting in a different direction (Figure 80).

FRAMING TERMS

In order more clearly to understand roof framing, we must first be familiar with the following terms, which the building trades student should commit to memory:

Span. The span of a roof is the distance between the outside corners of the wall plates (Figure 81).

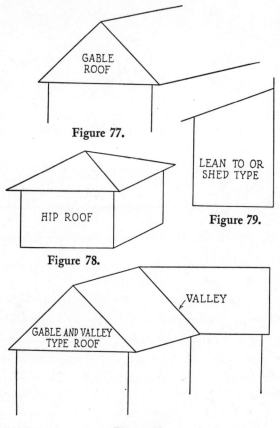

Figure 77.

LEAN TO OR SHED TYPE

Figure 79.

HIP ROOF

Figure 78.

VALLEY

GABLE AND VALLEY TYPE ROOF

Figure 80.

Run. The run of a roof is the shortest horizontal distance measured from a plumb line passing through the center of the ridge to the outer edge of the plate (Figure 81). The run is always equal to half the span, provided the building is of equal pitch.

Rise. The rise of a roof is the *vertical* distance from the top of the plate to the upper end of the measuring line or equal point on the ridge (Figure 81).

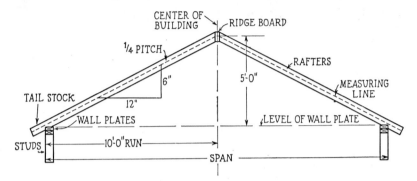

Figure 81. Illustration of framing terms.

A simple rule to follow for finding the rise of a roof when the pitch is known is

Multiply the pitch by the span.

Example: A building is 24 ft. wide. The roof pitch equals ⅓. What is the rise?

Solution: Rise equals $\frac{1}{3} \times$ 24 ft., or 8 ft.

Pitch. The pitch of a roof is the slant or slope from the plate to the ridge. It is usually expressed in terms of the ratio of the total rise to the total width of the building. Thus, if a building has an 8-ft. rise and a 24-ft. span, we would say 8 ÷ 24 = ⅓, or ⅓ pitch (Figure 82).

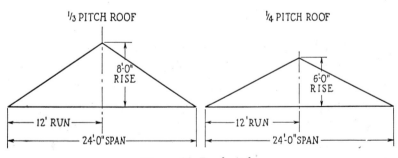

Figure 82. Roof pitch.

A simple rule for finding the pitch of a roof is

Divide the rise by the span.

Example: A building is 24 ft. wide (span). The rise of the roof is 8 ft. What is the pitch?

Solution: Pitch equals $\dfrac{8}{24} = \dfrac{1}{3}$, or ⅓ pitch.

PRINCIPAL ROOF PITCHES

The principal roof pitches are generally called "½ pitch," "⅓ pitch," and "¼ pitch." The rise for ½ pitch equals one-half the distance of the span; for ⅓ pitch, one-third the span; and for ¼ pitch, one-fourth the span.

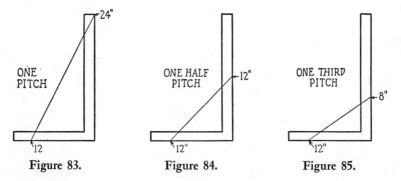

| Figure 83. | Figure 84. | Figure 85. |

Figures 83–85. The principal roof pitches are generally called ⅓, ½, and ¼, This means that the rise for ⅓ pitch would equal ⅓ the span. One-half pitch would equal ½ the span and ¼ pitch would equal ¼ the span.

If we stand a steel square on a table, with the body up and the tongue resting on the table, and construct a line from the figure 24 on the body to the figure 12 on the tongue, we have a slant or slope representing 1 pitch (Figure 83). If we draw the line from 12 on the body to 12 on the tongue, we have a slant equal to ½ pitch (Figure 84). If we draw the line from the figure 8 on the body to the figure 12 on the tongue, we have a slant equal to ⅓ pitch (Figure 85).

Thus figures on the body represent the inches of rise, and the 12 on the tongue represents 1 ft. of run. Thus a roof rises so many inches for each foot of run, and the number of inches it rises for

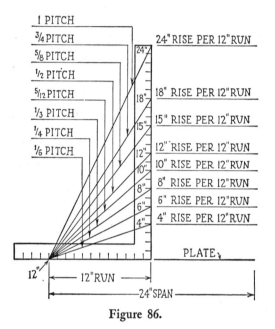

Figure 86.

each foot of run determines the pitch. For example, if 24 in. on the body and 12 in. on the tongue represent 1 pitch, 6 in. on the body would be $\frac{6}{24}$ of 1 pitch or $\frac{1}{4}$ pitch; 8 in. on the body would be $\frac{8}{24}$ of 1 pitch or $\frac{1}{3}$ pitch; 12 in. on the body would be $\frac{12}{24}$ of 1 pitch or $\frac{1}{2}$ pitch; 18 in. on the body would be $\frac{18}{24}$ of 1 pitch or $\frac{3}{4}$ pitch, etc. (Figure 86).

LENGTH PER FOOT OF RUN

Rafter tables found on a steel square are based on *rise per foot of run;* that is, the figures in the tables indicate the length of the rafters per 1-ft. run of common rafters for any rise of roof. Therefore, if the run of a building is 3 ft., the length of the rafter will be 3

times the figure listed under the rise (see Figure 87). The roof has a
6-ft. span and any given rise per foot. The figure is a right triangle,
ABC, with the run, rise, and rafter as its sides. The run of the rafter

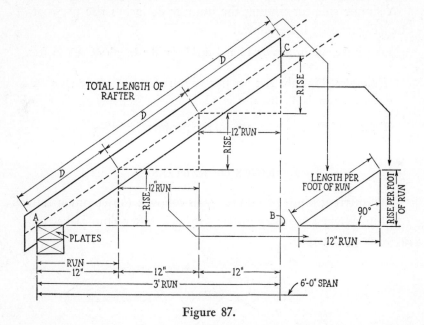

Figure 87.

is 3 ft. This being divided into 3 parts, each will represent a 1-ft.
run. If vertical lines are drawn through these points, you will find
that the rafter is also divided into 3 equal parts marked *D*. Since

Figure 88. A simple rule for finding
the number of inches rise per foot of
run is: multiply the rise in feet by 12
in. in order to obtain the total number
of inches in the rise. Divide the total
number of inches in the rise by the
length of run in feet. This will give
the rise per foot of run.

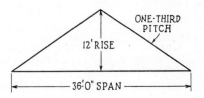

each section *D* represents the length of the rafter per foot of run
and the total run of the rafter equals 3 ft., the rafter would be as
long as 3 times *D*. By this method the length of any rafter for a

building of any width can be determined. The length per foot of run will be different for different-pitched roofs. In order to find the length of the rafter you must first know the rise per foot of run.

A simple rule for finding the number of inches rise per foot of run (Figure 88) is as follows:

Multiply the rise in feet by 12 and divide by the length of run in feet.

Example: Find the rise per foot of run of a roof whose span is 36 ft., run is 18 ft., rise is 12 ft.

Solution: $12 \times \dfrac{12}{18} = 8$, or 8-in. rise per foot.

KINDS OF RAFTERS

The different kinds of rafters are as follows: (1) common rafter; (2) hip rafter; (3) valley rafter; (4) jack rafter (hip jacks, valley jacks, cripple jacks).

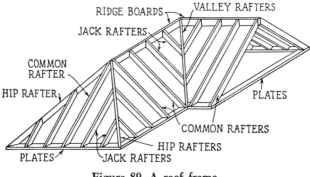

RIDGE BOARDS — VALLEY RAFTERS
JACK RAFTERS
COMMON RAFTER
HIP RAFTER
PLATES
COMMON RAFTERS
HIP RAFTERS
PLATES — JACK RAFTERS

Figure 89. A roof frame.

Common rafters are those that extend from the plate to the ridge at right angles.

Hip rafters are those that extend from the corner of the plate to the ridge diagonally.

Valley rafters are those extending diagonally from the plate to the ridge at a point where two roofs intersect.

Jack rafters are those that do not extend from the plate to the ridge. *Hip jacks* are those whose lower ends rest on the plate and the upper ends rest against a hip rafter. *Valley jacks* are those whose upper ends rest against the ridgeboard and whose lower ends rest against a valley rafter. *Cripple jacks* are those whose upper and lower ends touch neither the plate nor the ridge but are nailed in between a hip and a valley rafter.

For examples of rafters, see Figure 89.

RAFTER CUTS AND TERMS

In order to understand rafter framing thoroughly you should also know the various cuts found on rafters and the places to find them (Figure 90).

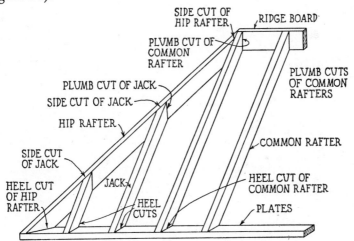

Figure 90. Rafter cuts and terms.

The top cut or plumb cut is the end that is placed against the ridgeboard at the ridge. If the ridge is omitted, it rests against the opposite rafter.

The seat cut, sometimes called the "bottom" or "heel" cut, is the end that rests on the plate.

The side cuts, sometimes called "cheek" cuts, are those made on a bevel at the side of a rafter so that they will fit against other members of the roof frame.

The length of a rafter is the shortest distance between the outer edge of the plate and the center of the ridge line.

The eave or tail is the part of the rafter that extends out past the outside corner or edge of the plate. It is never figured in determining

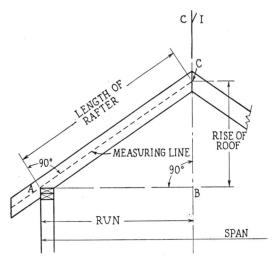

Figure 91. Measuring line of rafter.

the length of a rafter but must be considered in buying the material. The amount is determined from the plans or type of cornice to be used.

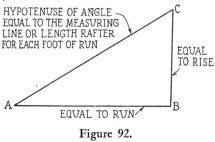

Figure 92.

The measuring line is an imaginary line drawn down the middle of the face of a rafter parallel to the edges. This line measures the length of the rafter (Figure 91). If we let a right triangle represent the roof *ABC* (Figure 92), the measuring line is the hypotenuse, or the longest side. The other two sides are the rise and the run.

HOW TO FIND THE LENGTH OF COMMON RAFTERS

To find the length of common rafters secure a steel square with a rafter table on the face (Figure 93). Then look on the first line below the outside edge of the blade which is marked "Length of common

	2|3	2|2	2|1	2|0	1|9	1|8
LENGTH OF COMMON RAFTER PER FOOT OF RUN						21.63
LENGTH OF HIP OR VALLEY PER FOOT OF RUN						24.74
DIFFERENCE IN LENGTH OF JACKS 16" ON CENTER						28.84
DIFFERENCE IN LENGTH OF JACKS 24" ON CENTER						43.27
FOR SIDE CUTS OF JACKS USE						6$^{11}/_{16}$
FOR SIDE CUTS OF HIPS OR VALLEYS USE						8$^1/_4$
	2|2	2|1	2|0	1|9	1|8	1|7

1|7	1|6	1|5	1|4	1|3	1|2
20.81	20.00	19.21	18.44	17.69	16.97
24.02	23.32	22.65	28.00	21.38	20.78
27.74	26.66	25.61	24.585	23.585	22.625
41.62	40.00	38.42	36.88	35.38	33.94
6$^5/_{16}$	7$^3/_{16}$	7$^1/_2$	7$^{13}/_{16}$	8$^1/_8$	8$^1/_2$
8$^1/_2$	8$^3/_4$	9$^1/_{16}$	9$^3/_8$	9$^5/_8$	9$^7/_8$
1|6	1|5	1|4	1|3	1|2	1|1

1|1	1|0	9|	8|	7|	6|
16.28	15.62	15.00	14.42	13.89	13.42
20.22	19.70	19.21	18.75	18.36	18.00
21.70	20.83	20.00	19.23	18.58	17.87
32.56	31.24	30.00	28.84	27.78	26.83
8$^7/_8$	9$^1/_4$	9$^5/_8$	10	10$^3/_8$	10$^3/_4$
10$^1/_8$	10$^3/_8$	10$^5/_8$	10$^7/_8$	11$^1/_{16}$	11$^5/_{16}$
1|0	9|	8|	7|	6|	5|

Figure 93.

rafter per foot of run." Under each of the numbers on the inch line at the top edge of the blade from 2 up to 18, you will find figures given in inches and hundredths of inches, the length per foot of run of rafters whose rise per foot of run is 2 or 18 in., or any number in between. For example, if the pitch is ⅓, the rise per foot of run

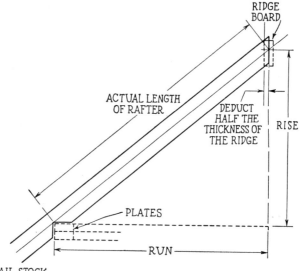

Figure 94. After the length of the rafter has been obtained, deduct half the thickness of the ridgeboard.

would be 8 in. Therefore, look under the figure 8 and find 14.42 in., which is the length of the rafter per foot of run for a ⅓ pitch roof. Therefore, to find the length of the common rafter multiply this length per foot of run by the actual number of feet in the run. If the run is 10 ft., 10 × 14.42 = 144.20, the length of the common rafter in inches. This divided by 12 gives 12.01, the length in feet. This is the actual length of the rafter. From this a deduction should be made for half the thickness of the ridgeboard, and to this should be added any additional stock for the tail rafter (Figure 94).

HOW TO OBTAIN THE TOP AND BOTTOM CUTS

You will note that the top and bottom cuts are always at right angles to each other (Figures 95 to 98). Therefore, if a large steel square is placed alongside the rafters, as in Figure 95, the edge of the

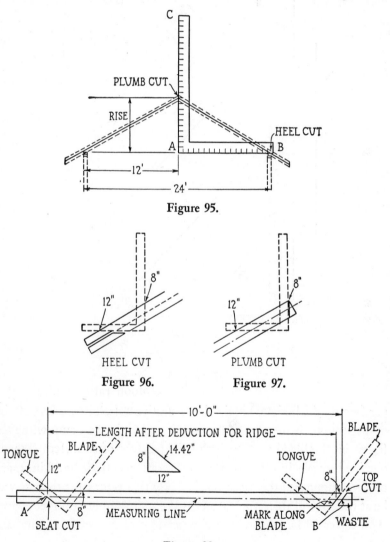

Figure 95.

Figure 96.   Figure 97.

Figure 98.

tongue will coincide with the heel cut or seat cut, and the edge of the body will coincide with the plumb cut. Therefore, line *AC* gives the *plumb cut,* and line *AB* gives the *seat cut.* However, a square is not large enough for this, so you use 12 in. on the tongue and the rise

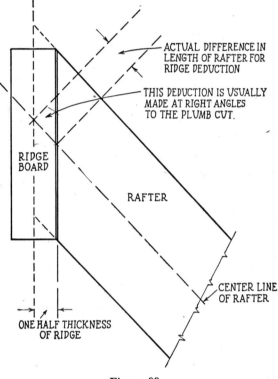

ACTUAL DIFFERENCE IN
LENGTH OF RAFTER FOR
RIDGE DEDUCTION

THIS DEDUCTION IS USUALLY
MADE AT RIGHT ANGLES
TO THE PLUMB CUT.

RIDGE
BOARD

RAFTER

CENTER LINE
OF RAFTER

ONE HALF THICKNESS
OF RIDGE

Figure 99.

per foot on the body to obtain the respective cuts. The distance 12 in. on the tongue is merely used as a unit and is the 1-ft. run, while the figure on the blade represents the *rise per foot of run.* Both cuts are obtained by placing the square on the rafter so that the 12-in. mark on the tongue and the mark on the body that represents the rise will be at the edge of the rafter, or stock. For an example, consider a common rafter 10 ft. long with a rise per foot of run of 8 in. Find the cuts (see Figure 98). Let the ends of the rafter be represented by points *A* and *B*. To secure the seat cut take 12 in. on the tongue and 8 in. on the body. Lay the square on the board so that the tongue will coincide with point *A*. This is the seat-cut line. Mark along the square and cut. For the top cut lay the square on so that the body coincides with point *B*. Mark and cut. Remember that the marks 12 and 8 in. must be kept accurately at the edge of the rafter while they are being located. Deduction for the ridge should be made, which is one-half the thickness of the ridge. This deduction is usually made at right angles to the plumb cut (Figure 99). Ridgeboard deduction ensures perfect fit and good construction.

HIP AND VALLEY RAFTERS

The hip rafter is one that forms a hip in the roof extending from the corner of the building diagonally up to the roof. The valley rafter

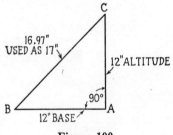

Figure 100.

is the same as a hip rafter except that it forms a valley where two roofs intersect.

A hip rafter may be compared to the diagonal of a square prism. Its relation to common rafters is the same as the relation of the hypotenuse of a right triangle to its sides. For example, if the two sides of a right triangle are each 1 ft., or 12 in., the hypotenuse will be 16.97 in., in rafter framing always taken as 17 in. See triangle *ABC* in Figure 100.

The prism in Figure 101 has a base 10 ft. square, of which one side represents the plate and the other the run of common rafter. Its height is 6 ft. 8 in., representing the rise of the roof.

Let *ACD* represent this triangle, *AC* the plate, *CD* the run of common rafter, *AD* the run of hip rafter, *CB* the common rafter, *AB* the hip rafter, *A* the corner of the building, *DB* the rise of the roof.

By taking 1 ft. of run of common rafter and 1 ft. length on the plate you will have a right triangle, whose other side represents a portion of the run of the hip rafter, which, of course, corresponds to 1 ft. of run of a common rafter. This will be 16.97 in., or commonly 17 in.

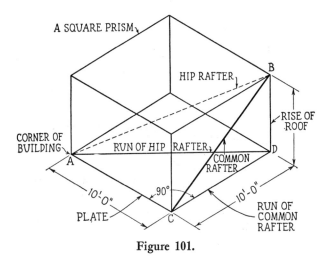

Figure 101.

HOW TO FIND THE LENGTH OF HIP OR VALLEY RAFTER

Look on the second line of the rafter table marked "Length of hip or valley per foot of run" (Figure 93) and multiply the length given there by the number of feet in the *run of the common rafter.* If the pitch is ⅓, you would look under 8 and find 18.76 in the second line. If the common rafter run is 10 ft., then the hip rafter will be as long as 10 × 18.76, or 187.60 in. This divided by 12 gives 15.63, the length of the hip rafter in feet.

Cuts. The top and bottom cuts can be obtained by using 17 on the tongue and the rise per foot of run on the body; 17 will give the seat cut, and the figure on the body will give the plumb cut.

Measuring. The length of all hips and valley rafters is measured along the center of the top edge or back.

Side cuts. At the ridge it is necessary to have side cuts on hip or valley rafters. Look in the last line of rafter table on the square where it is marked "For side cuts of hips or valleys use" (Figure 93). The figures given in this line refer to the graduation marks on the outside edge of the body. Take this figure and 12 in. on the tongue and mark the side cut along the tongue where the tongue coincides with the point on the measuring line.

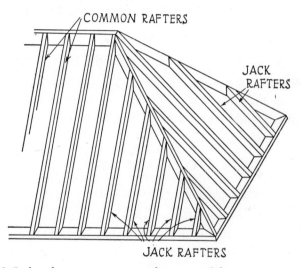

Figure 102. Jack rafters are common rafters cut off for some reason or other, perhaps because of intersecting roofs.

HOW TO FIND THE LENGTH OF JACK RAFTERS

Jack rafters are common rafters cut off for some reason or other. It may be because of intersecting roofs or on hip corners, etc. (Figure 102). Jacks rafters are spaced the same, have the same pitch, and lie in the same plane as common rafters. They also have the same length per foot of run as common rafters. Jack rafters are usually spaced either 16 or 24 in. on center. As they rest against the hip or valley on equal spaces, the second jack must be twice as long as the first; the third three times as long; etc.

If you look in the third line of the rafter table (Figure 93), you will find "Difference in length of jacks 16″ on center." If you look in the fourth line, you will find "Difference in length of jacks 24″ on center." The figure given under the rise per foot of run number is the length of the first and shortest jack. The second will be twice as long, etc. Multiply the figure given in the tables by the number indicating the position of the rafter. From this length subtract half the diagonal thickness of the hip or valley.

HOW TO MAKE SIDE CUTS FOR JACKS

Plumb and seat cuts for jack rafters are the same as for common rafters. Side cuts for jacks are found on the fifth line of the rafter table marked "For side cuts of jacks use." Take the figure shown in the table on the body and 12 in. on the tongue. Mark along the tongue for the side cut.

COLLAR BEAMS

Collar beams are pieces used as ties between rafters on opposite sides of the roof and designed primarily to stiffen it (Figure 103). They should not be expected to hold the building together. They

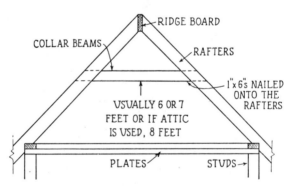

Figure 103. Collar beams are usually placed on every third rafter. They should be nailed on as the rafters are put in place. Care should be taken not to split the ends.

are usually placed well up on the rafters in order to leave headroom in the attic.

1. For light and medium roofs, use 1 by 6's.
2. For medium to medium heavy roofs, use 2 by 4's.
3. For heavy roofs, use 2 by 6's.

The length of a collar beam depends upon its position. Its most effective position is at mid-point. The length is usually taken from the blueprints. Collar beams are generally placed on every second or third rafter, as each pair of rafters is nailed in place. Care should be used in nailing on the collar beams so as not to split the ends.

3

ROOFING AND SIDING

The slope of the roof is very frequently the deciding factor in choosing roofing materials to be used and the methods necessary to put them into place. Modern roof design, especially in ranch-style architecture, along with necessity for economy in the use of materials has brought the slope of the roof down gradually, so that the predominating roof lines now are much lower in pitch than they were. The new roof lines frequently leave attic areas so low in headroom that they are practically useless except as limited storage spaces. The ultimate in shallow slopes for roofs is, of course, the flat roof.

This type of roof construction has made great gains and has been widely accepted in residential construction. However, a good flat roof really has a slight slope, even though this may be imperceptible to the eye. Thus the type of roof to be covered definitely decides the kind and style of shingle or other materials to be used for a roof covering. Roofing materials may be grouped as follows:

1. Wood shingles
2. Asphalt shingles or composition shingles
3. Slate and asbestos shingles

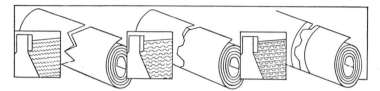

Imitation shingles made in rolls from roll roofing. These are applied in strips in the same manner as any other roll roofing.

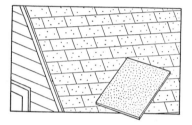

Asphalt slate-surfaced shingles cut into individual shingles. These are nailed on in the same manner as any other shingle.

Strip shingles come in various patterns. They are composed of two or more shingles combined into one piece.

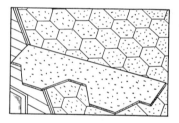

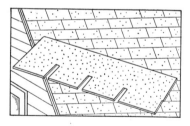

Strip shingles are usually notched or cut to look like individual shingles after they are nailed in place. They are notched at the factory at the time of manufacture.

Wood shingles may be used on the roof or on the side of the house. When used on the side of a house they are usually stained or painted.

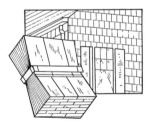

Figure 104. Types of roofing.

4. Roll roofing
5. Built-up roofing (paper)
6. Flashings (paper and metal)

Some of these materials are shown in Figure 104. Their purposes are very definite.

1. They provide a weather-resisting surface for the top of the house or building.
2. They exclude water and moisture from the building.
3. They keep out wind.
4. They lessen infiltration of dirt and dust.
5. They provide a definite amount of insulation.

WOOD SHINGLES

Definition. Wood shingles are thin, oblong, overlapping pieces of wood of various sizes used to nail onto the roof frame to provide a weathertight surface or roof.

Sizes. There are three different standard lengths of wood shingles recognized. These are 16, 18, and 24 in. Shingle lengths will vary some. It is customary to find various differences as much as 1 in. over or under the specified lengths.

The thickness of shingles at the butts varies with their length but is the same for all grades of the 16-in. length. Shingles 16 in. long must be so thick that five shingles, when measured across the butts, or thickest portion, when green will measure 2 full inches. These are known then as 16 in. 5/2 shingles. Five butts of 18-in. shingles measure 2 in. or 2¼ in. These are known then as 18 in. 5/2 or 18 in. 5/2¼ shingles. The longest commercial shingles made are 24 in. in length and the thickness at the butt is ½ in. Four such shingles will measure 2 full inches. These are known then as 24 in. 4/2 shingles.

Wood shingles are sold in three grades, No. 1, No. 2, and No. 3. Number 1 red-cedar shingles represent the best grade that is manufactured. They are intended for roof construction, where the shingles should lie flat and tight and where there must be complete protection from rain water driven by high winds. Number 2-grade shingles should be used only as undercoursing and for side-wall work. Number 3 shingles should be used only on outside walls and as undercoursing for better shingles.

Construction. Roof shingles should be spaced $\frac{1}{8}$ in. to $\frac{1}{4}$ in. apart. Wall shingles are laid on without spacing. The first course of shingles at the eaves should be doubled, and for all first-class work a triple layer of shingles is recommended. The second layer in the first course should be nailed over the first in such a way that the joints in each course are not less than $1\frac{1}{2}$ in. apart, the minimum side lap allowable, and if possible, should be broken by a greater margin. None of the joints in the three layers should match up or come over each other. On the first course the butts should project from 1 in. to $1\frac{1}{2}$ in. beyond the roof board or sheathing, so that the water will spill into the gutter and not down the side of the building.

As successive courses are applied, correct exposure should be measured from the butts of the shingles in the preceding course. At intervals it is a good plan to measure courses from the ridge, so that errors in the alignment of courses can be corrected by adjustments that will not be discernible to the unaided eye. When the last course has been nailed in place, that portion of the shingle projecting beyond the ridge should be sawed off.

When shingles are laid with the standard exposure of 5 in. to the weather, four bundles will cover 100 sq. ft. of area. In all roof construction, there should be at least three layers of wood shingle at every point, to ensure complete freedom from leakage. This means that there should never be more than one-third of the shingle exposed to the weather. The amount of exposure depends upon two things: the length of the shingle and the pitch of the roof. The steeper the roof pitch is, the longer the shingle will last, thus less exposure is not so essential.

For new construction work, use 3*d* nails for 16-in. and 18-in.

shingles, and 4*d* nails for 24-in. shingles. For overroofing longer
nails will be needed as the job demands.

Estimating wood shingles. The amount of shingles required to
cover the roof or walls of a building depends on such factors as
(1) the size of the building, (2) the type and design of the roof or
building, (3) desired exposure of the shingles, (4) methods of application. By exposure is meant the amount of the shingle that remains uncovered or exposed to the weather. This is determined by
the pitch of the roof. In column 3 of Table 16 are listed the various
recommended exposures of 16-in. shingles for typical roof pitches.

TABLE 16. ROOF-COVERING CAPACITIES OF 16-INCH SHINGLES

Roof pitch	Rise per foot of run, inches	Exposure of shingles, inches	Coverage for four-bundle square, square feet
Quarter pitch	6	3½	70
⁷⁄₂₄	7	4	80
⅓	8	4½	90
⅜	9	5	100
⁵⁄₁₂	10	5	100
1¹⁄₂₄	11	5	100
Half pitch	12	5	100
1³⁄₂₄	13	5	100
⁷⁄₁₂	14	5	100
⅝	15	5	100
⅔	16	5	100
¾	18	5	100
⅚	20	5	100
⅞	21	5	100
Full pitch	24	5	100

The area of a roof depends on the size, slope, and type. The usual types of roofs are the shed, gable, gambrel, arch, monitor, half monitor, combination, and hip (Figure 105). When estimating

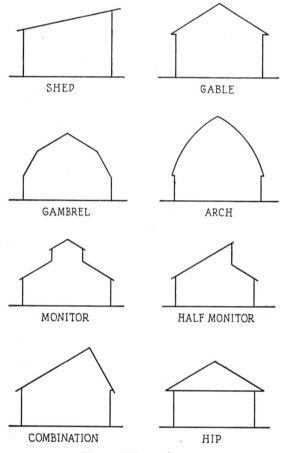

SHED

GABLE

GAMBREL

ARCH

MONITOR

HALF MONITOR

COMBINATION

HIP

Figure 105. Roof types.

amounts of shingles needed for a roof it is necessary to make extra allowances for such items as ridges, hips, valleys, and the double rows of starters at the eaves. An addition of ½ sq. ft. should be made for each lineal foot of eaves. For the valleys, hips, and ridges, an allowance of 1 sq. ft. for every lineal foot should be added. Valleys and hips of equal length cancel each other and require few additional shingles, as the cut sections from one may be used on the other.

The *gable* roof (Figure 106) is a ridge roof ending in a gable. To estimate the area for shingles, multiply the ridge length (R) by the length of the rafter (S). Multiply by 2, and make an allowance for the ridge and for the double row of shingles at the eaves.

For example, to find the area of the gable roof in Figure 106, which consists of two sides or slopes, multiply 20 ft. times 9 ft. This

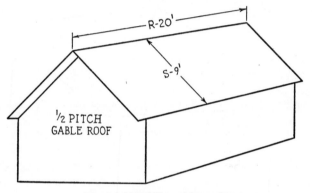

Figure 106. The gable roof.

gives the area of this side in square feet, or a total of 180 sq. ft. Then multiply this area by 2 for a total of 360 sq. ft. or the total area for both sides. Adding ½ sq. ft. for each lineal foot of the eave, ½ × 20 × 2 = 20 sq. ft., and add 1 sq. ft. for each lineal foot of ridge, 1 × 20 = 20 sq. ft., we find a total of 360 + 20 + 20 = 400 sq. ft. We see in Table 16 that shingles for this pitch roof can be exposed 5 in. and that one square will cover 100 sq. ft. so by dividing the total area, 400 sq. ft. by 100, the coverage per square, we find the answer to be 4, or 4 squares of shingles.

For further example, to find the area of the *hip* roof (Figure 107). Here we will need to figure one side or slope at a time and then multiply by 4. Thus we would multiply one-half the distance (S) 20 by the eave width (E.W.) 30, or 10 × 30 × 4 sides = 1,200 sq. ft. Add to this ½ sq. ft. per lineal foot of eaves for the double course and 1 sq. ft. per lineal foot of ridge and hip to find the total area in square feet. Thus we would have for the eaves, $\frac{1}{2} \times 30 \times 4$ sides = 60 sq. ft.; and for the four hips, $1 \times 24 \times 4$ hips = 96 sq. ft.; and for the roof, $10 \times 30 \times 4$ sides = 1,200 sq. ft., or a total of $60 + 96 + 1,200 = 1,356$ sq. ft.

From Table 16 we find that for a $\frac{1}{3}$-pitch roof, an exposure of $4\frac{1}{2}$ in. is recommended and that a four-bundle square of 16-in. shingles will cover 90 sq. ft. The total area of the roof in square feet,

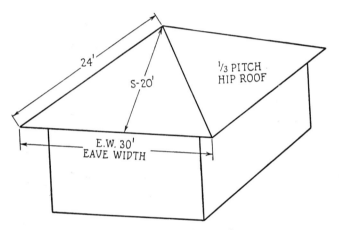

Figure 107. The hip roof.

with allowance for starters, ridges, and hips added, divided by 90 will give the number of four-bundle squares of 16-in. shingles required. Thus, $1,356 \div 90 = 15.06$ squares, or 15 squares and one bundle, or 61 bundles.

ASPHALT SHINGLES

Definition. Asphalt shingles (composition) are made from a felt-base material that has been treated on each side with asphalt. As asphalt itself is both waterproof and adhesive, the felt base is impregnated with it to form a waterproof and weatherproof material. The top side, or weather side, is usually imbedded with a coating of colored mineral granules that provides a finish surface, as well as adding durability to the surface.

Size. Asphalt shingles may be purchased individually or in strips. Individual shingles are usually 8 or 9 in. wide and 12 or 12½ in.

SPECIFICATIONS FOR ASPHALT SHINGLES

Size	Head lap, in.	Expose, in.	Weight per square, lb.	Shingles per square	Bundles per square
10″ × 36″	2	4	210	100	2
12½″ × 36″	4½	4	266	99	3
12″ × 36″	2	5	257	80	3

The above specifications are typical of the size, weight, lap, exposure, and number of shingles and number of bundles in a square. These, of course, vary with different manufacturers. Follow the manufacturers' instructions for nailing on whenever possible.

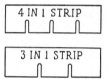

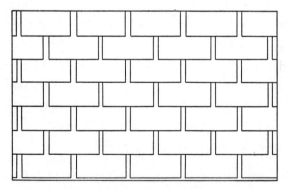

Figure 108. A pattern of composition shingles.

long. Strip shingles are made up usually of three or four combined into one piece and come in widths from 10 to 12½ in. The length of each is generally 36 in. These shingles are sold in bundles, usually laid 4½ to 5 in. to the weather. Two or three bundles will cover a square, depending on the thickness, the weight, and the number of strips. Good-quality strip shingles will weigh approximately 210 to 250 lb. per square. A pattern of asphalt or composition shingles is shown in Figure 108. Asphalt shingles are generally self-spacing, but an even distance for the weather lap should be maintained at all times.

How to nail on asphalt shingles.   A double course of shingles should be used at the eaves to start the work. This is true for both

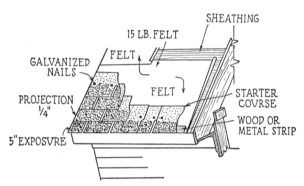

Figure 109. If a wood or metal strip is not used under the first course or starter course, another course of shingles may be used by nailing them on with slots up. This gives a double thickness at the eave. Always drive nails in directly over the slots.

asphalt and wood shingles. Asphalt shingles should be nailed on with galvanized, copper, or bronze nails, never with plain iron nails. Determine the amount of exposure to be used and lay the shingles to

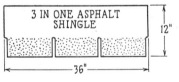

Figure 110.

a chalked line (Figure 109). Asphalt shingles should be laid on a tight deck, or a solid roof sheathing. For starting, lay a double row, or course, at the eaves, the first row with the slots up. Let these shingles project over the edge of the roof about an inch. Directly over this course lay another, with the slots downward. This provides a double thickness, and the 1-in. projection gives a good drip edge. In nailing always drive the nails in just over the cutouts or slots, up about

¾ in. Use large-head galvanized nails, about 1 to 1¼ in. long, unless circumstances require longer ones. Always start to nail at the center of the shingle. This prevents it from buckling. Ten-inch shingles should never be laid more than 4 in. to the weather; 12- and 12½-in. shingles, never more than 5 in. to the weather (Figure 110).

How to shingle up and over a dormer. Quite often, difficulty is experienced in laying on asphalt shingles of three-in-one or four-in-

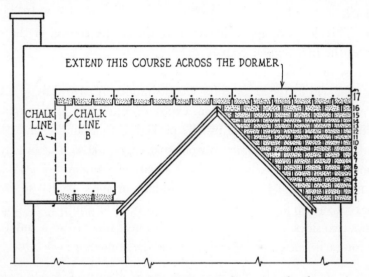

Figure 111. If the number of the course extending over the dormer is even, start the new course on chalk line *B*. If the number is uneven, start the new course on chalk line *A*.

one strips when shingling up on two sides of a dormer or of a small gable end that finishes into the main roof, and where there are no straight courses below for starters (Figure 111).

In order to ensure the break at the right place, it will be necessary to shingle up one side of the dormer until a course of shingles will clear the ridge of the dormer or the gable. Carry this course on across, as shown, and tack the last few shingles in place temporarily. Then proceed as follows:

1. Chalk a square and a perpendicular line (line *A*) from the end of the last shingle down to the eave or the edge of the roof.

2. Then measure back one-half single shingle width and chalk another line (line *B*), parallel to the first.

3. Now start at the bottom and count the courses that have been put on the other side.

4. If the number is even, like 2, 4, 6, or 8, start the new course at the bottom on line *B*.

5. If the number is odd, like 3, 5, 7, etc., start the new course on line *A*.

6. This does not apply, however, to the starter course, or the one under the first regular course.

How to estimate for asphalt shingles. Estimating for the *area* of the roof will be the same as for wood shingles. A strip shingle 12 in. by 36 in. laid with a 4- to 5-in. exposure will cover approximately 1 sq. ft. These shingles are usually packed 33 to a bundle, and three bundles will cover a *square* of roof surface, or 100 sq. ft., thus three bundles are considered and sold as a square of shingles. For example, to find the number of squares of asphalt shingles needed to cover the roof shown in Figure 106, we would need to multiply *R* times *S* times two sides, plus ½ sq. ft. for each lineal foot of eaves and 1 sq. ft. for each lineal foot of ridge. Thus the following:

$$20 \text{ ft.} \times 9 \text{ ft.} \times 2 = 360 \text{ sq. ft. surface}$$

$$1 \text{ ft.} \times 20 \text{ ft.} = 20 \text{ sq. ft. for ridge}$$

$$\tfrac{1}{2} \text{ ft.} \times 40 \text{ ft.} = 20 \text{ sq. ft. for eaves}$$

Therefore,

$$360 + 20 + 20 \text{ sq. ft.} = 400 \text{ sq. ft.}$$

$$\frac{400 \text{ sq. ft.}}{100} = 4$$

or 4 squares of shingles, or 12 bundles.

Roof terms. In working on roofs and applying shingles, it is well to know the various roof terms, what they mean and where they are found. Some of these are shown in Figure 112. Also shown (in Figure 113) are some methods for finding the areas of roofs of various shapes. It should be remembered that when ordering and estimating for shingles one must allow for a double course at the eaves and extra for caps on hips, ridges, etc.

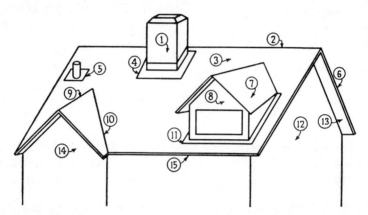

Figure 112. Roof terms: (1) chimney; (2) ridge; (3) main roof; (4) flashing; (5) vent; (6) verge; (7) dormer roof; (8) dormer gable; (9) ridge; (10) valley; (11) dormer flashing; (12) house gable; (13) rake projection; (14) house gable; (15) eaves.

How to lace a valley. Recent development in roofing application employs what is termed a "laced valley." Lacing the shingle courses as they intersect at the valley makes a neat, well-appearing application and saves material, such as metal-valley tin, copper, and other alloys. Lacing is done by nailing on the courses so that each course overlaps the other at the valley, as shown in Figure 114.

ASBESTOS SHINGLES

Definition. In size and colors asbestos shingles are very much the same as other shingles. They are, however, fireproof and very distinctive in appearance. They are made of asbestos fiber and portland cement. They cannot burn or wear out, rot or deteriorate to any extent from exposure to the weather, and they require very little if any maintenance.

Size. Asbestos shingles may be obtained in uniform or tapered thickness, with smooth or rough texture, and in various colors. They are made and sold by the square, which means sufficient shingles

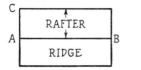

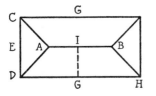

Gable Roof. Multiply the length of the ridge (*A* to *B*) by the length of the rafter (*A* to *C*). This gives the area of one side, which multiplied by two gives the total roof area.

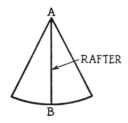

Hip Roofs. Multiply the length of the eaves (*C* to *D*) by one-half the length of the rafter (*A* to *E*). This gives the area of one end of the roof, which multiplied by two gives the area of both ends. For the sides, add the length of the ridge (*A* to *B*) to the length of the eaves (*D* to *H*): divide the sum by two and multiply by the length of the rafter (*I* to *G*). This gives the area of one side, which multiplied by two gives the area of both sides. The sum of the areas of both sides and both ends equals the total roof area.

Conical Towers. Multiply one-half the length of the rafter (*A* to *B*) by the distance around the eaves.

Circles

Diameter times 3.1416 equals circumference
Circumference times 0.3183 equals diameter
Diameter squared times 0.7854 equals area

Figure 113. Methods for finding the areas of roofs of various shapes.

to cover 100 sq. ft. of surface when applied in accordance with the manufacturer's directions. The number of shingles in a square varies considerably according to the type being used, as the lap varies greatly with the type. Usually eave starters, ridge and hip shingles, and ridge roll for the various types of asbestos shingles will need to be purchased separately, as all asbestos roofing pieces are of rigid material.

Application. Asbestos shingles are intended to be used on pitched roofs only. For a slope of less than 5 in. to the foot they are not

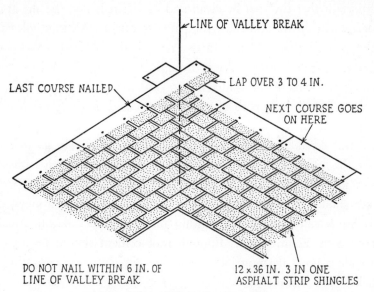

Figure 114. How to lace a valley.

recommended. When they are installed over wood sheathing, there should first be applied a layer of 15-lb. slater's felt, with lapped joints of at least 4 in.

ROLL ROOFING

Roll roofing is material similar to asphalt roof shingles, except that it is manufactured in rolls instead of in shingles. It comes in both a plain surface and a slate surface (Figure 104).

Its purpose is the same as that of shingles. Practically any type of roll roofing commercially available will keep out water, until the material begins to disintegrate. Its durability depends upon its thickness, proportions of ingredients, and conditions of service. Most rolls are made to cover 100 sq. ft., or 1 square. Weights vary from 50 to

125 lb. per roll or square. Widths vary from 12 to 36 in. Manufacturer's instructions should be carefully followed in regard to spacing and lapping. Never lap less than 2 in.

A great deal of care should be used in laying roll roofing. It is important that the roof be clean and dry. If it is not, the sheathing boards will shrink and cause the paper to buckle. All knotholes and other openings should have a covering of tin or sheet iron to prevent the paper from breaking through. In laying the roll or sheet, always work from the center out toward the ends. This allows the sheet to stretch before all of it has been nailed. It is a good plan to stagger the nails and thus prevent splitting of the sheathing boards. Lap the sheets according to the pitch of the roof. The steeper the roof, the less lap is needed. All laps should be secured with a smooth, even joint of the cement that is usually supplied with the paper. Care should be taken to flash around all openings, chimneys, etc. Flashings can be made by cutting pieces of the roll into squares about 8 by 12 in. square. Enough roof cement should be used to provide a good flashing job and to prevent water from seeping in back of the flashing.

BUILT-UP ROOFS

Definition. The most important function of a roof is to keep out the rain. Built-up roofs may consist of several layers of felt, asphalt, and roofing materials, all combined and applied as one piece. The number of plies used determines the length of time the roof will last. Three plies of asphalt felt properly applied to a roof with four courses of asphalt should give a roof that is good for at least 10 years; four plies, for 15 years; and five plies, for 20 years. After a built-up roof is completed and has had installed all the plies of felt and courses of asphalt, it should be covered with roof slag or gravel. This gravel keeps the sun away from the felt and prevents the asphalt and the felt from drying out and cracking.

Sizes. Most felts are manufactured in rolls 36 in. wide and of various lengths, with one or more squares per roll. The types, weights, and qualities are obtainable in most local lumberyards. Felt impregnated with asphalt and asbestos is considered the best.

Construction. Usually for commercial buildings with flat roofs the built-up roof is used. However, new ideas of design as applied

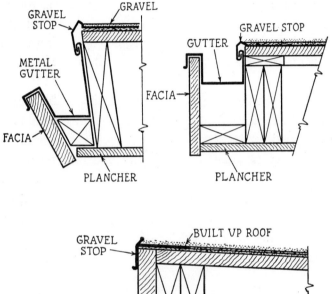

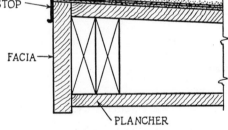

Figure 115. Built-up roofs with built-in gutters.

to the modern-type dwellings call for flat-roof construction with built-up roofs. A good flat roof does have some slant or slope, and provision must be made for the roof water by way of gutters. Built-up roofs for houses must be installed with gutters and gravel stops. The gutter is generally made as an integral part of the design and is built into the eaves of the roof (Figure 115).

FLASHINGS

Definition. Roof flashings are extremely important on a building. Wherever there is a change in roof lines, as at valleys where main roof lines intersect, or where dormer roofs and main roofs intersect, or wherever there is a projection above the roof such as a chimney or a plumbing vent, provision must be made for water runoff. Rain water must not be allowed to run down in these intersections and crevices, and this can be prevented by using metal flashings. The secret of the metal flashing is that it can be bent to follow the roof lines in both directions, with the valley thus formed acting as a channel for water runoff. Sometimes it is possible to lap shingling material to take the place of flashing, but in general the results are not so good.

A number of materials are available for flashing—tinned sheet metal, galvanized metal, sheet copper, and sheet aluminum. It is considered wise to use the copper or aluminum whenever possible. Tinned steel sheets will rust through very quickly, especially if the tinned surface has been broken or dented. If tinned or galvanized sheets are used, they should be painted regularly.

Sizes. Flashing materials will vary in size and weight according to the material being used. Tinned metal for flashing valleys, under windows, around chimneys, etc., is manufactured in rolls of various widths. The width needed depends on the place in which it is being used. The sizes in most general use are as follows:

1. For main valleys, 16 to 20 in.
2. For dormer valleys, 8 to 10 in.
3. For porch and house connections, 8 in.
4. For roof and shed dormers, 10 in.

Copper flashing is manufactured in rolls and is sold both by weight and by gage. The 16-oz. soft roofing temper is generally used (Figure 116).

Galvanized sheet-metal flashing is usually 26-gage 1.25-ounce zinc, coated per square foot and coated both sides. Lead may be either hard or soft, and the weight per square foot depends on the thickness used. This varies greatly. Copper-coated building paper (3-oz.) is used extensively over windows and frame openings.

Construction. Skill is necessary in the application of flashings. The metal must be applied in such a way that any water running downward will be deposited on top of the flashings, not underneath it. The water must have no chance to run backward. Once water has

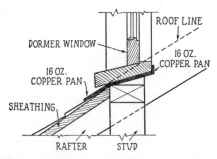

Figure 116. Installation of copper pan, or flashing, under dormer window.

been deposited on the flashing, the flashing must allow the water to run off over the shingles, not under them. Care must be taken with masonry chimneys. The joints must be raked out in steps following up the slope of the roof, and the flashing step cut and fitted into the raked joints, then sealed with a mastic so that water cannot run underneath the flashing or into the chimney joints. Sometimes step flashing may be laid into the bricks or masonry as the chimney is being built.

How to flash around a chimney

1. Cut off two pieces of metal flashing about 18 in. wide and long enough to bend back to fit the sides of the chimney. The length will depend on the width of the chimney (Figure 117).

2. These are called the front-apron and the rear-base flashing.

3. Imbed these well in roof mastic and nail them in place.

4. Step-flash the sides with metal flashing material or with metal shingles cut and bent so that they will extend under each course

of roofing shingles on the lower end and also into the deep cutout mortar joints in the chimney.

5. Now wedge the metal flashing securely into the open joints in the brick and refill the joints with cement or roof mastic (Figure

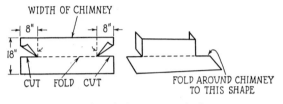

Figure 117. Flashing around chimney.

118). A cricket should be built on the high side of the chimney, so that it will receive the broadside wash from the roof.

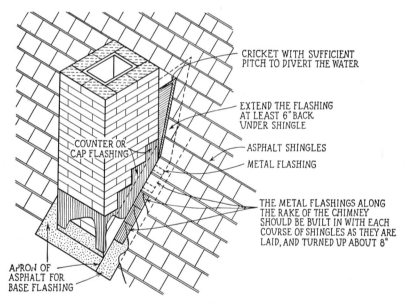

Figure 118. Installation of flashing around chimney.

How to flash pole gutters. When installing or relining pole gutters, use a good weight of valley tin or a heavy-weight slate-surfaced roofing paper. Nails should not be used in any part of the watercourse. Joints should be at least 9 in., with the run or slope of the gutter. If made of metal, all joints should be soldered. If made of asphalt slate-surfaced paper, they should be well imbedded in roof cement (Figure 119).

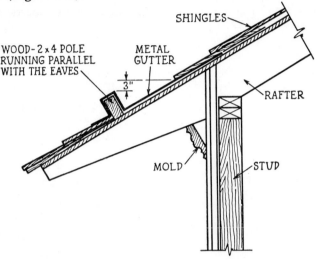

SHINGLES

WOOD-2x4 POLE
RUNNING PARALLEL
WITH THE EAVES

METAL
GUTTER

3"

RAFTER

MOLD

STUD

Figure 119. Installation of pole gutter.

Flashing parapet walls. In flat-roof construction, correct flashing is a very important item. Parapet walls, coping, drains, skylights, supports, and braces, all come in for correct and needed flashing. Common methods for flashing flat roofs are shown in Figure 120. Wherever possible, cap flashing should extend through the wall or across the wall under the coping. Cant strips should always be used in the angles at the walls to form a break and lessen the angle. Flashing blocks are considered very good, but must be set in as the wall is being built.

WALL SHINGLES

Definition. Wall shingles are much the same as roof shingles. They may be of wood, asbestos, asphalt, or other trade compositions.

Wood shingles for side walls are made almost entirely of red cedar, white cedar, cypress, or redwood, and come in sizes as shown in Table 17.

Asbestos wall shingles are nailed on in much the same manner as wood wall shingles, except that they do not lap over on the ends. Instead, they have felt strips at the ends to seal the joints (Figure

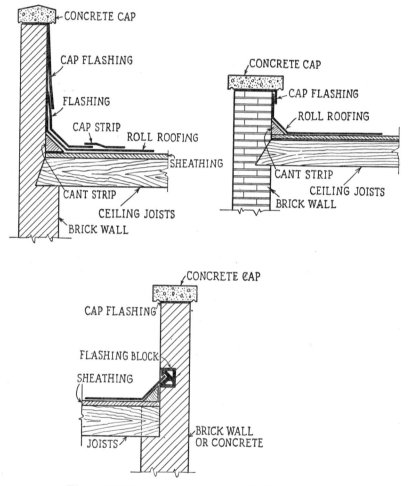

Figure 120. Common methods for flashing flat roofs.

121). They are also secured with rustproof nails. The corners must be well fitted and lapped to make tight joints.

Asphalt wall shingles should be spaced and applied in accordance with the manufacturer's directions. However, construction in general is the same for all side-wall shingles.

TABLE 17. SIDE-WALL COVERING CAPACITIES IN SQUARE FEET FOR THE VARIOUS-SIZED SHINGLES—FOUR-BUNDLE SQUARES

	Single course				Double course *		
Exposure, inches	16″	18″	24″	Exposure, inches	16″	18″	24″
7	140						
7½	150			11½	226		
8		146		12	238	218	
8½		154		13		236	
9			120	14		254	
10			132	15			200
11			146	16			212
11½			152				

* Quantities shown are for each course.

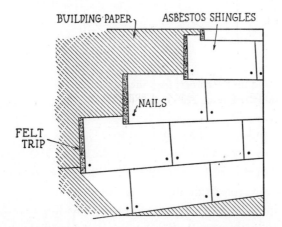

Figure 121. Asbestos shingles are nailed directly onto the side of the house. They are generally nailed on over building paper and laid to a chalk line. Joints are on halves.

How to apply wood side-wall shingles. Wood shingles should be spaced no less than $\frac{1}{4}$ in. apart. Two or more nails in each shingle should be used and put near the edge. Nails should be hot-dipped zinc or copper alloy. All shingle courses should be started at

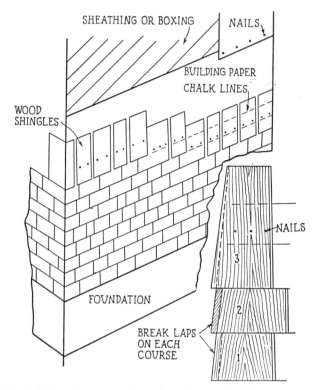

Figure 122. Build up the corners first, then draw a chalk line from the butt of each corner shingle. Lay on each course to a chalk line.

the foundation line with a double course. Courses should be laid out so that shadow lines will coincide with the upper and lower lines of the window openings. Corners of the building are laid out first, and then chalk lines or straightedges are used to nail the rest of the course on, in order to keep them in a straight line.

1. Start nailing on wall shingles by applying the first course at the bottom, or foundation.

2. Double the first course and drop the butts of the shingles down below the foundation line, at least 1 in. (Figure 122).

3. Lay the shingles onto a chalk line or a straightedge tacked onto the wall.

4. Break all joints back 1 to 2 in. or more for wood shingles.

5. At the corners break the laps on each course.

Estimating side-wall shingles. When computing the quantity of shingles required for side walls, subtract the number of square feet of openings from the total number of square feet of wall surface. Openings of less than 10 sq. ft. should be disregarded. When wood shingles are applied to side walls, there are usually two thicknesses, compared with three for roofs. Thus fewer shingles are required to cover a square, or 100 sq. ft. The usual exposure for 16-in. shingles on side walls is 7½ in. for single coursing and 12 in. for double coursing. A four-bundle square of 16-in. shingles laid 7½ in. to the weather will cover 150 sq. ft.; laid 12 in. to the weather, it will cover 238 sq. ft. As the latter exposure requires double coursing, another four-bundle square of No. 2 shingles would be required for the undercourse.

Running-inch method of estimating wall shingles. Another method of figuring shingles required is the running-inch method. The length of each row in inches times the number of rows, as determined by the exposure and size of area, will give the running inches of shingles required for roofs or side walls. Table 18 gives the number of running inches per four-bundle square. Allowance should be made for starters, hips, valleys, ridges, and deductions for openings.

WOOD WALL SIDING

Definition. Wood siding is lumber cut to various patterns and sizes. Quite often it is called "weatherboarding." It is the material or layer of special milled boards that forms the outside surface of a frame wall. The purpose of wall siding is to keep out the wind and weather, to help keep a building warm on the inside, and to

TABLE 18. NUMBER OF RUNNING INCHES PER FOUR-BUNDLE SQUARE
OF SHINGLES

Length of shingle, inches	Thickness green, inches	Green	Dry
16	5 butts, 2	2,960	2,880
18	5 butts, 2¼	2,664	2,620
24	4 butts, 2	1,996	1,920

increase the strength of its construction. The proper selection of the kind and grade of siding for outside wall coverings is important. It should be of a decay-resisting species that will hold tight at the joints and will take and hold paint well. It should by all means be well-seasoned lumber. Good siding is available in the following species: western red cedar, white pine, and fir.

Sizes. Siding is made in sizes ranging from ½ in. by 4 in. to ¾ in. by 12 in., and is available in most species at most retail lumberyards.

There are *two* general kinds of siding: (1) bevel siding (Figure 123), and (2) drop siding (Figure 124).

Bevel siding is available in 4-, 5-, 6-, 8-, 10-, and 12-in. widths. *Drop* siding is available in 4-, 6-, 8-, 10-, and 12-in. widths.

As a rule, siding boards do not come in definite given lengths but in random lengths. Siding is usually manufactured and tied together in bundles of a given number of square feet per bundle. The amounts in these bundles will also vary according to their lengths.

Construction. In applying wood siding, all joints around windows and doors or other openings should be carefully and well fitted. All spliced joints should be absolutely tight, to prevent the infiltration of air and moisture. All spliced joints should have a small strip of waterproof paper behind them with the bottom end of the paper

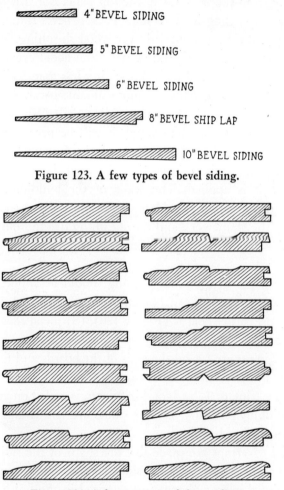

4" BEVEL SIDING

5" BEVEL SIDING

6" BEVEL SIDING

8" BEVEL SHIP LAP

10" BEVEL SIDING

Figure 123. A few types of bevel siding.

Figure 124. A few patterns of drop siding.

lapped out over the top edge of the underneath board. Spliced joints should never be made directly over each other. Proper nailing with nails of the correct size is important. Nailing should always be directly over each stud. Siding may be applied directly onto the studs, over solid-wood sheathing or equal, over fiberboard, over gypsum board, or over insulating boards. Where sheathing is omitted, the stud walls should be well braced with let-in strips of 1 by 4 running diagonally from the floor sill to the top plate. For this type of construction, drop siding is more suitable than bevel siding.

When wood siding is applied over wood sheathing, joints can be made anywhere. Siding should be nailed on about every 16 in. with 8*d* hot-dipped galvanized nails. For siding less than ¾ in. thick, 7*d* hot-dipped galvanized nails are more suitable because they are less likely to split the wood. Do not set siding nails. When any kind of sheathing is used other than wood, it will be necessary to use the regular let-in braces at the corners of the frame. This gives the added strength required. The siding material should be thoroughly dry before it is applied. The walls of the building also should be dry and the siding should never be applied soon after a rainstorm. Let the framework and the sheathing dry thoroughly; otherwise there will be shrinking, buckling, nails pulled loose, open joints, etc.

At the corners of a building, siding should be applied in one of the following constructions: (1) miter joints (Figure 125), (2) butt joints against corner boards (Figure 126), (3) metal-covered corners (Figure 127).

1. Miter joints are cut on the ends of the boards and fitted against each other at the corners.

2. Corner trim, or 1- by 3- or 4-in. pieces, is nailed on at the corner of the building vertically. Against these are nailed and butted the ends of the siding boards.

3. Metal coverings are made just the shape of the siding and are nailed on at the corners over the siding boards. They cover the joint, can be painted over, and remain unnoticed in the finish. They also make waterproof corners and prevent the corners from opening up later or from showing, if they do open.

Application of wood siding should start at the foundation. However, in some cases, especially in high gables, it is started at the top and worked down. The courses should be laid out, or "storied," so that the shadow lines will coincide directly with the upper and lower

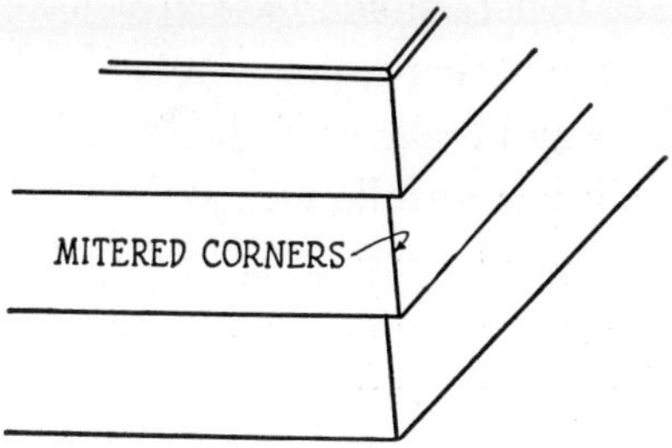

Figure 125. Siding boards mitered
at the corners.

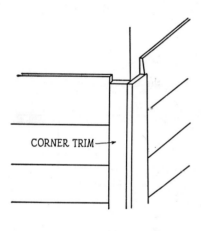

MITERED CORNERS

Figure 126. Siding cut and fitted to
corner trim at the corner of the wall.

CORNER TRIM

Figure 127. Metal corners are
used to cover up the joints and
to keep out moisture.

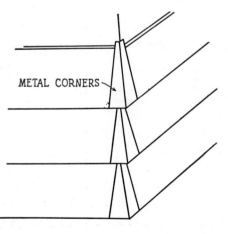

METAL CORNERS

lines of the window frames. It is well to work to a chalk line and to see that each course is kept level.

Estimating siding. When estimating siding, count the solid surface and make no deductions for openings. The proper lap for bevel siding is as follows:

1. 4-in. siding, lap ¾ in.
2. 5-in. siding, lap 1 in.
3. 6-in. siding, lap 1½ in.
4. 8-in. siding, lap 1½ in.
5. 10-in. siding, lap 1½ in.
6. 12-in. siding, lap 1½ in.

TABLE 19. COMPUTING FOR BEVEL SIDING AND DROP SIDING

Find the total area in square feet to be covered, and multiply by the conversion figure below.

Size, inches	Kind	Conversion figure
½ × 4	Bevel siding, ¾″ lap	1.50
½ × 6	Bevel siding, 1″ lap	1.40
½ × 8	Bevel siding, 1½″ lap	1.333
¾ × 8	Bevel siding, 1½″ lap	1.333
¾ × 10	Bevel siding, 1½″ lap	1.25
¾ × 12	Bevel siding, 1½″ lap	1.25
¾ × 6	Drop siding, 5″ face	1.20
¾ × 6	Drop siding, 5½″ face	1.10

To find the amount of siding needed, compute the area to be covered in square feet and do not deduct for openings unless they are extremely large, as in picture windows, wall windows, etc. After the total area in square feet has been determined, multiply this figure by the conversion figure in Table 19. For example, the surface of a house to be covered with ½-in. by 8-in. bevel siding has a total area in square feet of 4,125. By referring to Table 19, we find for this material, with a 1½-in. lap, a conversion figure of 1.333. Thus 4,125 × 1.333 equals 5,499 sq. ft. of siding needed, or approximately 5,500 sq. ft.

4

LATH AND PLASTER

Plaster bases, regardless of their kind, are applied directly to the studs of the walls. Their purpose is to form a base or wall surface onto which the plaster can be applied. Plaster itself is not elastic and, whatever the type of lath base used, will crack if there is any decided settlement or change in the walls or frames that hold it. Therefore, a solid, rigid houseframe, with proper and sufficient grounds installed, is the first essential to a good plastering job.

There are *three* general types of plaster bases or plaster lath in use. They are:

1. Gypsum lath (rocklath, sheetrock, etc.)
2. Wood lath
3. Metal lath

The type of construction being used will usually determine the types of lath or plaster bases needed.

GYPSUM LATH

Definition. Gypsum lath may be of three general types: (1) rock-lath, (2) insulating rocklath, (3) sheetrock. *Rocklath,* a gypsum board used for a plaster base, is made by casting a core of gypsum between a tough fibrous paper covering. The usual size is ⅜ in. by 16 in. by 32 or 48 in. The lath is nailed directly to the studs and forms a perfect bond with gypsum plasters. It may be purchased in "standard" or "perforated" sheets and is usually packaged or put up in bundles of six pieces, with a total of 32 sq. ft. to the bundle. In some areas it is packed five pieces to the bundle, with a total of 3 sq. yd. to a bundle.

Perforated rocklath is identical in all respects with the plain, except that perforations are provided at regular intervals. These perforations allow the applied plaster to mushroom through the holes and to form keys on the back. These keys mechanically key the plaster to the wall. Perforated lath is applied in the same way as the plain, or "standard." Sizing and packaging are the same as for the plain lath.

Insulating rocklath is the same as standard, except that on the back is mounted a thin sheet of bright aluminum foil. When it is applied with the foil side next to the frame and facing an air space ¾ in. deep or more, its insulating value is equal to that of ½-in. fiber insulating board.

Sheetrock is in general the same as rocklath, inasmuch as it is a regular plaster base. It is made in large, lightweight units which fit standard spacing in wood-frame construction. Plain sheetrock may be obtained with square edges or recessed edges. It may be plain or insulated with aluminum foil. It may be obtained in a plain finish and plastered over, the same as any other gypsum lath. It comes in sizes ¼, ⅜, and ½ in. thick; 4 ft. wide; and 6, 7, 8, 9, 10, 11, and 12 ft. long.

How to put on gypsum lath

1. Prepare a scaffold built on sawhorses or other means, just high enough for you to stand upon and reach the ceiling. Use 2- by 10-in. walk boards.

2. Nail the rocklath on, face out, with the long dimensions at right angles to the framing members of the walls.

3. Nail on the ceilings first.

4. Stagger all joints. Do not let any two ends break together on the same stud (Figure 128).

5. After the ceiling has been put on, start *down* the sides, working from the ceiling toward the floor.

6. Cut all gypsum lath with an old saw or score it with a pocket-knife and break it off.

7. Use up all scraps and pieces whenever possible, instead of cutting more whole pieces.

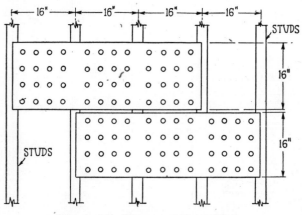

Figure 128. How to apply rocklath.

8. Drive five large-head lath nails into each stud or ceiling joist, through the rocklath.

9. Cut out and fit carefully around all electric receptacles, outlets, openings, etc.

10. If the doorjambs have been set, fit the lath up neatly to them and do the same for the window frames.

The size of the nails needed depends upon the thickness of the materials being used. For this see Table 20. The nails should be placed about ⅜ in. in from the edge and from 5 to 8 in. apart. All lath nails should be cement-coated.

WOOD LATH

Definition. Wood lath is a plaster base made from strips of wood. The laths are nailed directly onto the studs of the frame wall.

TABLE 20. NAIL QUANTITIES AND SIZES FOR ROCKLATH *

Nails	Type of boards			
	Gypsum board, ½ in.	Rocklath, ⅜ in:	Insulating lath, ⅜ in.	Sheet-rock, ¼ in.
Type nail..................	5d	4d	4d	4d
Pounds per 1,000 ft..........	6	4½	4½	4½
Size head..................	¹⁵⁄₆₄	⁷⁄₃₂	⁷⁄₃₂	⁷⁄₃₂
Gage......................	13½	14	14	14
Nails per pound..............	365	488	488	488

* All gypsum lath nails to be cement-coated.

Sizes. Wood laths are usually ⅜ in. thick, 1⅜ in. wide, and 32 or 48 in. long. They are generally sold by the thousand and weigh about 335 lb. for the 32-in. size and about 500 lb. for the 48-in. size per thousand.

All wood lath should be of good quality, and grades less than No. 1 should not be used. White-pine or cypress laths are preferable when they can be obtained. They should never have back or sap edges.

Construction. In nailing laths on the wall, space them about ⅜ in. apart in order to allow the plaster to be squeezed through the cracks and form keys on the back. These keys hold the plaster on. Laths should be nailed to and over all studs. Threepenny wire lath nails are used for wood lath.

Nail on seven rows of lath and then break over one space of studs and nail on seven more (Figure 129). Never run laths over or behind a partition. Using a low scaffold, nail laths on the ceilings first, then on the side walls from the top down.

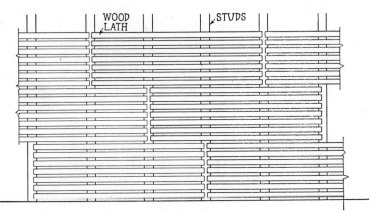

Figure 129. Method of spacing wood laths on studs. Nail on seven laths and then break over one space of studs and nail on seven more. Nail on the ceilings first, then nail on the side walls.

METAL LATH

Definition. Metal lath is made from sheet metal, perforated for use as a plaster base or lath instead of other materials. Metal lath comes in sheets, usually 27 by 96 in., either painted or galvanized. Standard weights are from 2.2 to 3.4 lb. per sq. yd. (Figure 130).

Construction. Metal lath is nailed directly to the studs with a sufficient lap. Some of the metal plaster laths are backed with a high-grade, waterproof construction paper. A large mesh should never be used for wall plastering, because it may cause wall cracks. A good, stiff lath should be used. All sheets should be well lapped and nailed. The minimum weights for metal lath should be as follows:

1. For wood studs, 2.2 lb. per sq. yd.
2. For ceilings on wood joists, 2.75 lb. per sq. yd.

3. For steel studding, 2.5 lb. per sq. yd.

4. For suspended ceilings, 3 lb. per sq. yd.

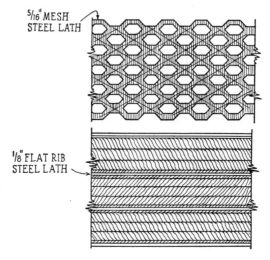

⁵/₁₆" MESH STEEL LATH

⅛" FLAT RIB STEEL LATH

Figure 130. Metal lath.

CORNER BEAD AND CORNER LATH

Corner bead (Figure 131) is used on vertical and horizontal corners and edges, in rooms, over wood and gypsum lath. It provides a definite edge to which to finish the plaster. It also serves as a protection to a corner that has been plastered and helps to form more accurately the shape of arched doors, openings, etc. It usually comes in stock lengths 6, 7, 8, 9, 10, or 12 ft. long. It is made mostly in 26 gage and weighs about 200 lb. per thousand feet. It is nailed on the corners with lath nails over the laths.

Corner lath is nailed in all the inside angles of a room. It is cut in strips about 4 in. wide and bent to a right angle (Figure 132). Its purpose is to prevent cracks in the plaster at the angles.

Metal door arches are used a great deal now in plastered openings, because they are installed very quickly and present a much neater finished job than do the ones built up from wood and covered with corner bead (Figure 133).

1. Nail all corner bead, corner lath, or metal arches on after the other lath has been applied. Nail them on over the other lath.

2. Use regular lath nails.

3. Cut all bead, corner lath, etc., with tin snips.

Figure 131. Corner bead provides a definite edge against which to finish the plaster. It also helps to form more accurately the shape of doors and other openings.

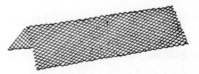

Figure 132. Corner lath is nailed in all the inside angles of the room.

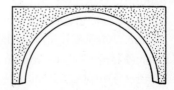

Figure 133. Metal door arches are used a great deal in plastered openings.

PLASTER GROUNDS

Plaster grounds. Plaster grounds are strips of wood, dressed, usually about 1 by 2 in., and nailed directly to the framework at points where needed. They are the same thickness as the finish plaster, usually $1\frac{3}{16}$ in. Their purpose is to provide a guide for the

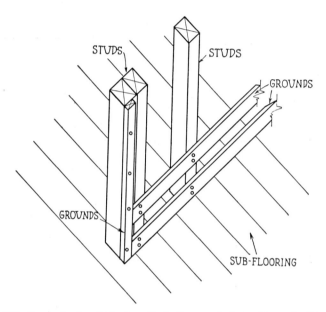

Figure 134. Grounds should be installed all around the walls at the floor. They are 1 by 2's, $\frac{3}{4}$ in. thick. They ensure a smooth edge to plaster to and a firm base on which to nail the finish trim.

plasterer and to avoid uneven plastering. In some cases the inside trim is nailed directly to the grounds; in others, as around doors, they are removed. Window frames often act as their own guide or grounds. Wherever finish wood trim comes in contact with plaster, some sort of grounds should be used.

Base. Grounds should be installed all around the walls at the floor (Figure 134). Sometimes one and sometimes two are used. This ensures a smooth surface on which to nail the baseboard and base mold. It also provides a solid surface on which to nail.

Doors. Grounds should be installed at all doors, inside or outside, where finish or trim is to be used. This ensures a snug fit and a smooth solid surface to which may be nailed the trim. In cheap work where it is customary to use the doorjamb itself for a ground, the jamb must be set before plastering. This usually results in the following objectionable situations:

1. The corners of the jambs become rough.
2. A clean sharp corner is impossible.
3. Wood becomes scratched.
4. Frame becomes injured by tools, lumber, etc.
5. Frame gets wet and swells, grain raises, etc.

It is much better to apply temporary grounds for the doors and tack them in place securely. Most carpenters make a guide for this work. It is a frame made the exact width of the wall after the plaster has been put on. This is set square and plumb, and the grounds are aligned to it. Most frame walls finish to 5¼ in. thick. A common practice is to use wood laths for door grounds, but 1- by 2-in. strips are much better.

Window grounds. Double-hung frame windows usually provide a ground in themselves. Casement frames are largely the same as door frames in that the grounds may be set first or the frame may be used. For all masonry walls and special construction, the problem of grounds must be worked out wherever wood trim is to be used.

Miscellaneous grounds. All such work as chair rails, dadoes, wainscoting, panels, picture molds, and mantels should have grounds, the size, of course, depending upon the work.

How to mark studs. It is always necessary to mark the location of all studs on the subfloor with a heavy crayon or by driving a large-head shingle nail into the floor before the plaster is put on. This aids in nailing on the base and mold later when the studs are covered.

DRY WALL CONSTRUCTION

Definition. A demand for faster and more economical construction has brought into wide usage a system of applying materials for finished walls known as "dry wall construction." This is a system of applying a single or double thickness of gypsum wallboards that need not be plastered.

Sizes. There are three thicknesses of gypsum wallboard—$\frac{1}{4}$, $\frac{3}{8}$, and $\frac{1}{2}$ in. The length varies from 4 to 12 ft. The $\frac{1}{4}$-in. board is made with square edges only. The $\frac{3}{8}$-in. standard gypsum board and the $\frac{1}{2}$-in. wallboard are available with square, beveled and recessed edges. The $\frac{1}{2}$-in. board, having a larger gypsum core, provides additional fire resistance, strength, and sound deadening. Insulating gypsum wallboard is made with all types of edges and thicknesses. Aluminum foil is firmly attached to the back surface of this material to provide reflective insulation and inhibit vapor condensation.

Construction. Gypsum wallboard requires a level, square, and true framework. The studs should be properly spaced and made plumb. The studs should be straight and have their faces in line with the top and bottom wall plates. All studs and joists should be spaced not more than 16 in. on center unless $\frac{1}{2}$-in. wallboard is being used. Even then 16-in. spacing makes for better construction. The ends and corners of all wallboard must be securely nailed.

Window and *door* frames will need to be ordered for the $\frac{3}{8}$-in. or $\frac{1}{2}$-in. grounds, whichever is being used, instead of the usual $\frac{3}{4}$-in., as no plaster is to be applied. It is altogether essential to plan a layout of each room before starting, to determine the number of pieces needed, their sizes, and how they can be best applied without waste. This is done by drawing a rough sketch of each wall and the ceiling (Figure 135). Blocking will be necessary behind all horizontal joints, between the studs.

How to apply single-thickness dry wall. After the sketches of each wall and the ceiling have been made, to determine the size of each piece, proceed as follows:

1. Start with the ceiling.
2. Use $\frac{1}{2}$-in.-thick recessed-edge wallboard.
3. Span the entire width of the ceiling if possible.

4. Apply the board at right angles to the ceiling joists.
5. Use 5*d* cement-coated nails, 1⅝ in. long.
6. Start nailing at the center of the board and work outward.
7. Space the nails ⅜ in. in from the edge of the board.
8. Space the nails about 5 to 7 in. apart.

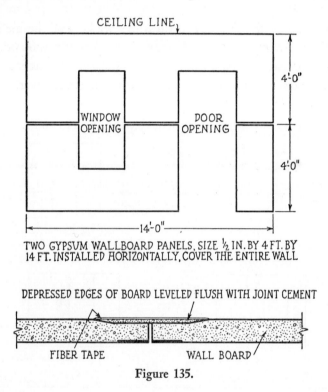

CEILING LINE

WINDOW OPENING   DOOR OPENING

4'-0"

4'-0"

14'-0"

TWO GYPSUM WALLBOARD PANELS, SIZE ½ IN. BY 4 FT. BY
14 FT. INSTALLED HORIZONTALLY, COVER THE ENTIRE WALL

DEPRESSED EDGES OF BOARD LEVELED FLUSH WITH JOINT CEMENT

FIBER TAPE   WALL BOARD

Figure 135.

9. Do not break the surface of the board by the blow of the hammer.

10. To cut the wallboard, first score the surface with a sharp knife. Snap the core by pressing down on the edge of the board. Then cut the back paper and break it by snapping the loose piece upward.

11. Smooth all cuts with sandpaper for neat jointing.

12. Use a keyhole saw for all irregular cutouts, such as arches.

13. When the ceiling is on, start the side walls at the top.

14. Span the entire width of the wall with one piece if possible.

15. Hold all boards tightly against the studs while nailing. This ensures against loose nailing.

16. Fit the lower boards neatly to the wall but do not wedge them. This breaks the boards and makes a weak construction.

17. Seal all joints (see "How to tape joints for dry wall construction").

How to apply the double-thickness dry wall. The double-thickness dry-wall system calls for two layers of gypsum wallboard, each one ⅜ in. thick. The base layer is nailed vertically to the studs and the face layer is applied horizontally over the base layer, with a

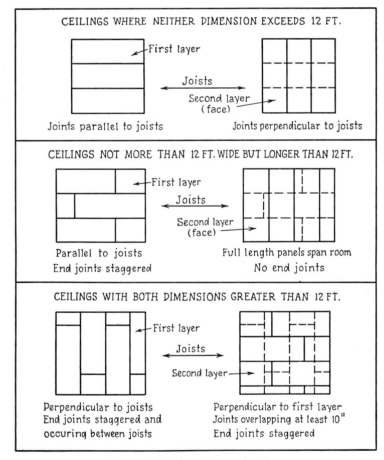

Figure 136. Three types of ceiling.

special adhesive which makes the two adhere to each other. The joints are sealed with a reinforcing tape and a special cement for this purpose.

The size and shape of the ceiling will largely determine methods of applying gypsum wallboard on any ceiling. It is essential to plan a layout of the walls and the ceiling of each room to determine the number of pieces that will be needed, and their sizes.

Each ceiling will fall into one of *three* types shown in Figure 136, thus permitting erection by one of the three methods. In all

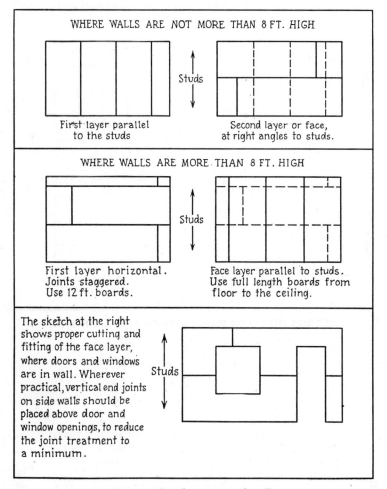

Figure 137. Three types of wall.

cases the face layer is applied at right angles to the direction of the first layer. The shape and size of the side walls will also determine the methods of application. Any wall will fall into one of the *three* types shown in Figure 137.

When the number of pieces and their sizes have been determined, proceed as follows:

1. Start by applying the first piece of base wallboard to the ceiling.

2. Nail on the first layer parallel to the ceiling joists.

3. Span the entire width of the room with one piece if possible. If this is not possible, stagger the end joints.

4. After the first layer has been applied to the ceiling, do the side walls. Nail the boards on parallel with the studs.

5. Start the application of the face layers. Nail all face layers on at right angles to the base layers. Special adhesive, supplied with the boards, is mixed and spread on the backs of the face layer with a notched trowel. This "buttered side" is then placed against the base coat and nailed in place.

6. Use only enough nails in the face layer to hold it in place.

7. Drive the nails in so that the heads are slightly below the surface of the wallboard, or if not so dimpled, they may subsequently be countersunk.

8. Seal all joints and nail holes (see "How to tape joints for dry wall construction").

How to tape joints for dry wall construction. Gypsum wallboard joints can be so well concealed that it is impossible to see them once the walls are decorated. The two principal materials required are perforated-paper joint tape and joint cement. These materials may be obtained along with the purchase of the wallboard. A good joint cement should be used, one which mixes easily. Good cement comes in dry powdered form, is uniform in texture, and sands down smoothly and easily. The perforated joint paper tape is a material that is applied over the joints in the wallboard after they have been prepared with the cement.

When mixing the cement, be sure to follow the manufacturer's directions closely. Luke-warm water should be used and the cement added to it gradually while being stirred. This plaster cement is mixed to a consistency slightly thinner than putty. Only the amount to be used the same day should be mixed.

The following steps are necessary to ensure a good installation of the joint tape:

1. With a 4-in. flexible putty knife, fill the recessed channel formed by the butted edges of the wallboard with the properly prepared joint cement.

2. Then press the perforated tape into the cement, using enough pressure to force the cement through the holes in the tape.

3. After this first coat has hardened, apply a skim coat of cement over the tape and feather it out as smoothly as possible.

4. Allow the filled joint to harden at least 24 hr.

5. Then with the use of No. 00 sandpaper on a wide sanding block, sand the joint down smooth and level with the surface of the wallboard.

6. Apply the tape at the inside corners by folding it along the center to a crease and then using the same application as for any other joint.

7. For outside corners, fold or crease the tape and apply it to both sides of the corner in the same manner as for the regular joints. If the edges of the boards do not meet, fill the space with putty before applying the tape.

8. To make a straight corner, keep the tape stretched tight as it is applied.

9. Before starting to conceal the nailheads, make sure the board is tight against the framing.

10. Fill the depressions around the nailheads, as well as any holes left by setting nails, with the first coat of cement.

11. After drying, apply a second coat.

12. For perfect concealment, a third coat is recommended.

13. Sand down all the filled surfaces to a smooth finish.

5

FINISH—TRIM, WINDOWS, AND DOORS

Inside finish or trim is that part of the construction usually consisting of the following:

1. Doorjambs
   a. Sides
   b. Head
2. Door trim
   a. Side casings
   b. Head casings
   c. Stops
   d. Back bands (not always used)
3. Window trim
   a. Side casings
   b. Head casings
   c. Stool
   d. Apron
   e. Stops
   f. Mullions (for more than one window)

4. Baseboard
   a. Baseboard
   b. Base molds
   c. Base shoe
5. Doors
   a. Inside
   b. Outside
6. Built-in cabinets
   a. Kitchen cabinets
   b. China cases
   c. Bookcases
   d. Linen cases
   e. Storage cases
   f. Ironing board
7. Floors
   a. Hardwood
   b. Softwood
8. Miscellaneous
   a. Clothes chute
   b. Telephone
   c. Mailbox
   d. Built-in recesses
   e. Fireplace mantels
   f. Breakfast nooks, seats, etc.

DOORJAMBS

Definition. Doorjambs are the linings or the sides of the openings (Figure 138) that form doorways. Their purpose is to provide a finished surface for that part of the doorway. To the jambs are nailed the casings and stop; on them are hung the doors.

Size. Doorjambs are made of stock usually ¾ in. thick for inside jambs and 1⅜ in. thick for outside jambs. The width, usually 5¼ in., may vary slightly, since the jambs should be just as wide as the plastered walls are thick. Inside jambs are usually built up with a stop ⅜ by 1⅜ in. nailed to the jamb to shut the door against. Outside jambs are usually rabbeted out to receive the door.

Rough openings for doorjambs are usually made in frame walls 2½ in. larger each way than the size of the door to be hung. This allowance is for *plumbing* and *leveling* of the jambs.

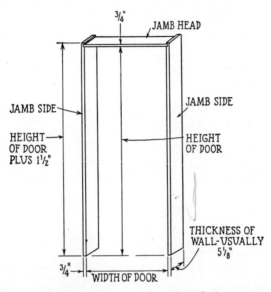

Figure 138. Doorjambs are linings, or the sides of the openings, that form the doorways. Their purpose is to provide a finished surface for that part of the doorway. On the jambs are nailed the casings and the stop. The doors are also hung on the jamb.

How to make and set a doorjamb

1. Regardless of how carefully rough openings are made, it is always necessary to plumb the jambs and level the heads, when jambs are set.

2. Rough openings are usually made 2½ in. bigger each way than the size of the door to be hung. For example, a 2 ft. 8 in. by 6 ft. 8 in. door would need a rough opening of 2 ft. 10½ in. by 6 ft. 10½ in. This extra space allows for the jambs, the wedging, and the clearance space for the door to swing (Figure 139).

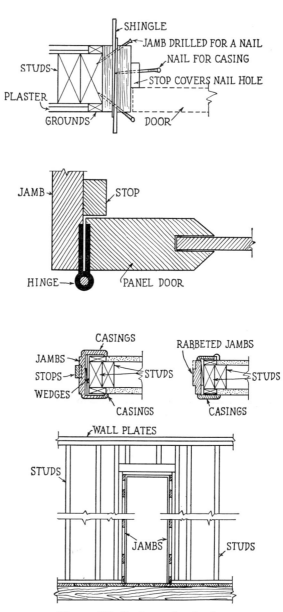

Figure 139. Setting a doorjamb.

3. Level the floor across the opening to determine any variation in floor heights at the point where the jambs rest on the floor.

4. Now cut the head jamb with both ends square, having allowed the width of the door plus the depth of both dadoes and a full $\frac{3}{16}$ in. for door clearance.

5. From the lower edge of the dado, measure a distance equal to the height of the door plus the clearance wanted under it. Mark and cut square.

6. On the opposite jamb do the same, only make additions or subtractions for the variation in floor, if any.

7. Now the jambs and jamb heads are nailed together with 8d common nails through the dado into the head jamb.

8. Set the jambs into the opening and place small blocks under each jamb on the subfloor just as thick as the finish floor will be. This is to allow the finish floor to go under.

9. Plumb the jambs and level the jamb head.

10. Wedge the sides with shingles between the jambs and the studs, to align, and then nail securely in place.

11. Take care not to wedge the jamb unevenly.

12. A straightedge 5 or 6 ft. long is used inside the jambs to help prevent uneven wedging.

13. Check jambs and head carefully, as jambs placed out of plumb will have a tendency to swing the door open or shut, depending on the direction in which the jamb is out of plumb.

DOOR TRIM

Definition. Door trim is material nailed onto the jambs and plaster around the door to provide a finish. It is frequently called "casing" (Figure 140). Its purpose is to provide a finish between the jambs and the plastered wall. Sizes vary from $\frac{1}{2}$ to $\frac{3}{4}$ in. in thickness, and from $2\frac{1}{2}$ to 6 in. in width. Narrow trim has become very popular, especially in the economy-built houses and ranch-style houses (Figure 141). Plain moldings are replacing the more elaborate shaped and curved material. Popular sizes and shapes are shown

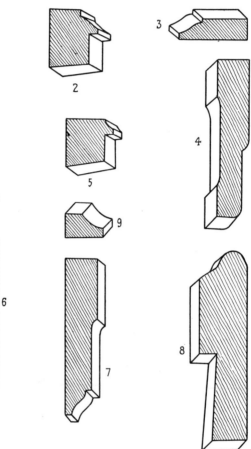

Figure 140. Door trim or casing: (1) picture mold; (2) cap mold; (3) window stop; (4) window and door casing; (5) chair-rail cap; (6) baseboard; (7) chair rail; (8) window stool; (9) base shoe.

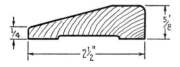

Figure 141. Section of a very popular style, modern trim for door openings, windows, and baseboards.

in Figure 140. Many modern designs call for the same size of trim or casing for the doors, windows, and baseboards. Most trim has a concave back, to fit over uneven plaster. In mitered work, care must be taken to make all joints clean, square, neat, and well fitted.

How to case up a door opening

1. If the trim is to be mitered at the top corners, you will need a miter box, miter square, hammer, nail set and block plane.

2. Leave a margin of ¼ in. from the edge of the jamb to the casing all around, as shown in Figure 142.

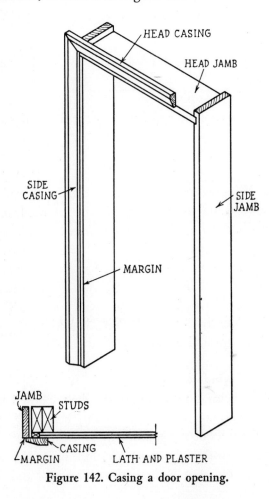

Figure 142. Casing a door opening.

3. Cut one of the side casings square and even at the bottom, with the bottom of the jamb.

4. Cut the top or mitered end next, allowing $\frac{1}{4}$ in. extra in length for the margin at the top.

5. Nail the casing onto the jamb and even with the $\frac{1}{4}$-in. margin line, starting at the top and working toward the bottom.

6. Use 4d finish nails along the jamb side and 6d or 8d case nails along the outer edge of the casings. The nails along the outer edge will need to be long enough to go through the casing and plaster, and into the studs.

7. Set all nailheads about $\frac{1}{8}$ in. below the surface of the wood with a nail set.

8. Now apply the casing for the other side and then the head casing, in order.

9. Avoid making hammer-head marks in the surface of the casings, as they give a very bad appearance to the finish, if not removed.

WINDOW TRIM

Definition. Window trim or casing is the material or pieces nailed onto the window frame to form a finish between the frame and the plaster. It usually consists of the same material that is used to case up the doors, plus the apron and the stool (Figure 143).

Sizes. Sizes for casing vary. They are usually the same as for the rest of the house trim. They may be $\frac{5}{8}$ in. to $\frac{3}{4}$ in. thick and $2\frac{1}{2}$ in. to 4 in. wide. Narrow casings are very popular. The stool is usually $1\frac{1}{8}$ in. thick by 3 to 5 in. wide, depending upon the style being used. The apron is generally of the same material as the casings.

How to trim a window

1. Cut and fit the stool into and around the window jambs.

2. Allow a projection of equal amount, both in front of the jambs and to the sides of the jambs. This is usually about 1 in.

3. Lower the bottom sash into place and adjust the stool to it. Leave a clearance of about $\frac{1}{8}$ in. between the stool and the sash.

4. Nail the stool into place. Use 8*d* finish nails and nail the stool onto the subsill of the window.

5. Cut the side casings off square on the ends, stand them up in place and mark them for the right length. Window casings are

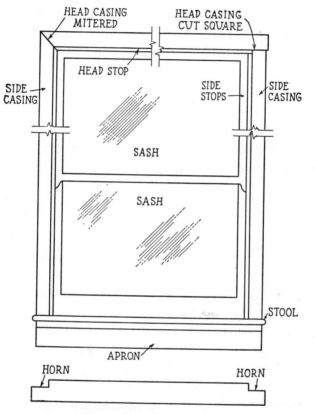

HEAD CASING
MITERED

HEAD CASING
CUT SQUARE

HEAD STOP

SIDE CASING

SIDE STOPS

SIDE CASING

SASH

SASH

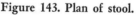

STOOL

APRON

HORN

HORN

Figure 143. Plan of stool.

nailed on even and flush with the inside of the window frame. If the corners are to be mitered, use a miter box. If no miter box is available, mark the casing off with a miter square and cut with a backsaw.

6. Nail the side casings into place. Use 4*d* or 6*d* finish nails on the jamb side and 8*d* finish nails on the outer edge or stud side.

7. Set all nails, as they are driven, with a nail set.

8. If a mullion is used (double window), fit and nail it into place.

9. Cut and fit the head casing into place.

10. Cut and fit and nail into place the window stops.

11. These are usually mitered at the top and square on the bottom. The stops are to hold the sash in place. Leave a clearance between the stops and the sash of approximately $\frac{1}{16}$ in. The sash should operate without binding anywhere.

BASEBOARD, MOLD, AND SHOE

Definition. Baseboard is usually a plain or molded piece of wood about $\frac{1}{2}$ to $\frac{3}{4}$ in. thick and $2\frac{1}{2}$ to 6 in. wide. Its purpose is to provide a finish at the junction of the floor and the wall and to

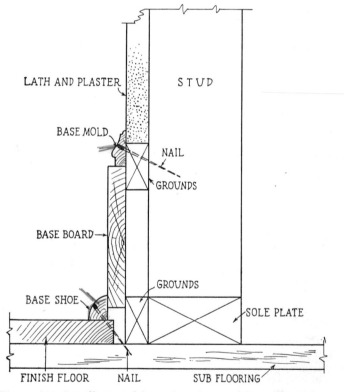

Figure 144. Installation of base shoe, base mold, and baseboard.

protect the wall finish from harm. It may or may not be accompanied by a mold at the top called a "base mold," and a shoe at the
bottom, called a "shoe mold" (Figure 144). Sometimes one or both
molds are omitted. When the base mold is omitted, the top edge of
the baseboard is usually molded in imitation of some form of mold.

How to install baseboard

1. Arrange, if possible, to have cuts occur only at corners, intersections, doorways, etc. This prevents the need for splicing.

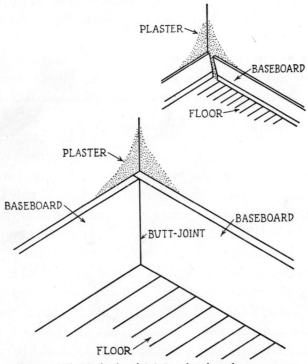

Figure 145. Methods of joining baseboards at corners.

2. Interior corners should be scribed and butt-jointed on the ends
(Figure 145).

3. Exterior corner cuts should be mitered and nailed to each other.

4. As the baseboard is cut and fitted it should be nailed to the
studs with 8d case nails, at least two nails to a joint. Baseboard wider
than 4 in. should have three nails to each joint.

5. Set all nails as they are driven. Never allow the hammer head to touch the wood, as this will leave marks in the wood.

6. If the finish floor has already been installed, the baseboards may be set directly onto the floor as they are nailed. If the finish floor is to be installed after the baseboard is on, it will be necessary to hold the baseboard up from the floor for this. This can be done by placing blocks of wood under the baseboard as it is being nailed into place. The size of the block depends on the thickness of the floor that is to be placed under the baseboard later. The blocks are temporary and should be removed as soon as the baseboard is in place.

7. As a rule, all trim in the house except the base shoe is nailed into place before the finish floors are laid, regardless of their kind.

8. The base shoe is nailed down after the finish floor is completed.

9. As the baseboard is nailed to the studs, it will be necessary to mark the studs' location on the subfloor in some manner, as the plaster hides them. This should be done before the plaster is put on. One method is to drive large-headed shingle nails directly in front of each stud, out about 3 or 4 in. They are easy to find after plastering and can be left in the subfloor and covered with the finish floor.

How to install base mold. Base mold is a piece of molding nailed to the top edge of the baseboard. Its purpose is to conceal irregularities in the plastered wall and give a finished edge to the baseboard and the plaster. Some baseboards do not require this, as they have a molded edge on the top.

Base molds vary in size according to the baseboard being used. For $1\,3/16$-in. baseboard, the mold should not be more than $5/8$ in. thick. The width of the mold is a matter of choice. All cuts in the mold should be made at the corners, at doors, or at places not readily noticeable. There are *two* methods of making cuts or joints at the interior corners: (1) mitering (Figure 146) and (2) coping (Figure 146). Coped joints are considered better because, if they open up, the crack is not noticeable. For exterior corners mitering is, of course, used. The nails used should be long enough to go through the mold and the plaster, and into the studs. It is usually necessary to drill holes for these nails, as they are liable to split the molding.

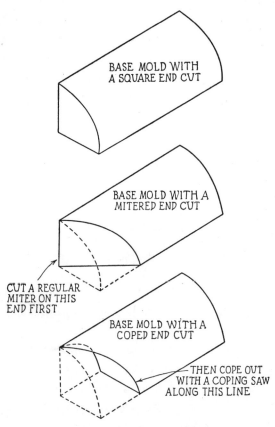

BASE MOLD WITH
A SQUARE END CUT

BASE MOLD WITH A
MITERED END CUT

CUT A REGULAR
MITER ON THIS
END FIRST

BASE MOLD WITH A
COPED END CUT

THEN COPE OUT
WITH A COPING SAW
ALONG THIS LINE

Figure 146. Base mold.

How to install base shoe. Base shoe is a molding nailed at the intersection of the baseboard and the *finished* floor. Its purpose is to cover or conceal the crack there (Figure 144).

Sizes vary for base shoe, but they are usually about ¾ in. by ¾ in. or ⅝ in. by ¾ in.

Construction is the same as for base mold. Use nails that are long enough to reach into the subfloor. This prevents the shrinking of the baseboard from pulling the shoe up from the floor (Figure 144).

Base shoe also is usually cut and fitted by the coping method (Figure 147).

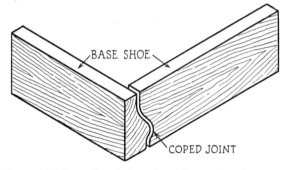

BASE SHOE

COPED JOINT

Figure 147. Base shoe is best fitted by coping the joints.

FINISH FLOORS

Definition. The finish floor is that which serves as the last or final floor to be laid and becomes the actual wearing surface. It may be laid over the subfloor but is sometimes laid directly onto the joists, where no subfloor is used. The purpose is to provide a surface for floor wear.

Even in small-house construction there are many types of floors, such as hardwood, softwood, wood blocks, etc., all with different textures, grades, thicknesses, widths, and lengths. Of these, the following have been selected as the best for the small house or average home:

1. Yellow pine
2. Oak (white and red)
3. Maple
4. Birch

Wood flooring is classified according to the method of sawing. It may be

1. Quartersawed (edge grain) (Figure 148)
2. Plain sawed (or slash sawed) (Figure 148)

As a rule, maple and birch are not sold as quartersawed. *Edge-grain* flooring gives much the most wear. It is cut so that the edge of the grain is presented as a wearing surface. It does not splinter and is hard and extremely durable. *Plain-sawed* or flat-grain flooring may be cut from the same log, but because of the direction of the grain it will be less durable.

Figure 148. Wood floor-ing is classified according to the method used in sawing it. When sawed from the logs as shown at **A,** it is classified as flat grain, or flat sawed. When sawed as at **B,** it is classified as quarter-sawed, or edge grain. Edge grain wears much better than flat grain and does not shrink as much.

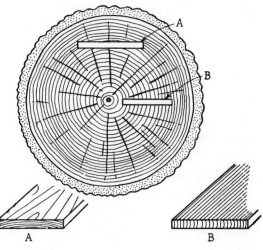

Most *softwood* flooring is graded as follows:

1. "A" and "B and better," stain, varnish, wax, or natural.
2. "C" and "D," stained dark or painted.
3. No. 1 and No. 2, for subfloors and rough or hard usage. "A" and "B and better" are generally used for finish floor work.

Standard sizes for softwood flooring are $2\frac{5}{32}$, $1\frac{1}{16}$, or $1\frac{5}{16}$ in. thick, and $1\frac{1}{2}$, $2\frac{3}{8}$, $3\frac{1}{4}$, $4\frac{1}{4}$, or $5\frac{3}{16}$ in. wide. Lengths run from 8 to 16 ft. The average small-house owner usually selects $2\frac{5}{32}$ by $2\frac{3}{8}$ in., with edge grain.

Most *hardwood* flooring is graded as follows:

1. Clear grade
2. Select grade
3. No. 1 common
4. No. 1 common and better shorts
5. No. 2 common

Standard sizes for oak flooring are $\frac{3}{8}$ by $1\frac{1}{2}$ in., $\frac{3}{8}$ by 2 in., $\frac{1}{2}$ by $1\frac{1}{2}$ in., $\frac{1}{2}$ by 2 in., $1\frac{3}{16}$ by $1\frac{1}{2}$ in., $1\frac{3}{16}$ by 2 in., $1\frac{3}{16}$ by $2\frac{1}{4}$ in. Oak is generally considered the best hardwood for flooring, $1\frac{3}{16}$ by $2\frac{1}{4}$ in. being the most desirable size.

There are several types of hardwood-floor installations, among which the following will be described:

1. Hardwood strip flooring over wood subflooring
2. Hardwood strip flooring over concrete slab floors
3. Hardwood block flooring over wood subflooring
4. Hardwood block flooring over concrete slab floors

How to install hardwood strip flooring over wood subflooring

1. Do not start to lay the finish floor until all other finish and trim work is done.

2. Do not start to lay the finish floor until all plastering is done and well dried.

3. Be sure the building is dry and that the flooring material is dry and is kept dry during the installation.

4. Before starting to lay the floor, clean the subfloor and cover it with a layer of heavy waterproof deadening felt, 15 lb. or better. Lap this paper at least 3 in. For better installations use a double thickness of paper all over.

5. Start at one side of the room and face-nail down the first flooring strip to a chalk line drawn parallel to the wall or lengthwise with the room (Figure 149). If the subfloors are not plywood or boards installed at diagonals, the finish floor strips should be nailed down at right angles or crosswise to the subflooring. If the subfloors are of plywood or nailed onto the floor joists diagonally, the finish floor may be run in any direction.

6. Lay the first strips with the groove side to the wall and even with the plaster finish. It is well to leave at least a $\frac{1}{2}$-in. margin all along the wall for expansion of the flooring.

7. Always use case nails of sizes indicated in Table 21, page 170.

8. The rest of the flooring should be nailed down by toenailing through the tongue (Figure 149).

9. Set all nails with a nail set. This allows the next board to be pulled up easily for a tight joint.

10. Toenail the strips into place, but do not damage the edges of the flooring with the head of the hammer.

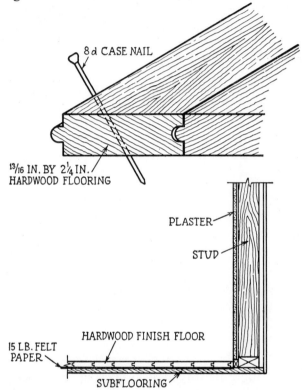

Figure 149. Lay hardwood flooring over 15-lb. felt paper. Toenail through the tongue edge with 8*d* case nails.

11. Nails should be placed not farther apart than 12 in.

12. Stubborn pieces of flooring may be driven home with a scrap or block of wood.

13. After the floor is laid, put down the base shoe.

14. Scrape and sand the floor in preparation for finishing.

How to install hardwood strip flooring over poured-concrete slab floors. With the popular concrete-slab-floor house has come a new

TABLE 21. FLOORING DATA

Kind	Thickness, inches	Width, inches	Per cent added	Size of case nails
Oak........	$1\frac{3}{16}$	$1\frac{1}{2}$	50	8d
	$1\frac{3}{16}$	2	$37\frac{1}{2}$	8d
	$1\frac{3}{16}$	$2\frac{1}{4}$	$33\frac{1}{3}$	8d
	$1\frac{3}{16}$	$2\frac{1}{2}$	$33\frac{1}{3}$	8d
	$\frac{3}{8}$	$1\frac{1}{2}$	$33\frac{1}{3}$	4d
	$\frac{3}{8}$	2	25	4d
	$\frac{1}{2}$	$1\frac{1}{2}$	$33\frac{1}{3}$	6d
	$\frac{1}{2}$	2	25	6d
Maple......	$\frac{25}{32}$	$1\frac{1}{2}$	50	8d
	$\frac{25}{32}$	2	$37\frac{1}{2}$	8d
	$\frac{25}{32}$	$2\frac{1}{4}$	$33\frac{1}{3}$	8d
Pine........	$\frac{25}{32}$	$2\frac{3}{8}$	27	8d
	$\frac{25}{32}$	$3\frac{1}{4}$	23	8d
	$\frac{25}{32}$	$5\frac{3}{16}$	15	8d

method for installing hardwood strip flooring. It may be installed over this slab as follows:

1. Lay down a pattern of staggered sleepers on the slab. These should be laid in mastic provided for this type of construction (Figure 150).

2. The sleeper on each side of the room at the wall will need to be continuous, to pick up the ends of the flooring.

3. The sleepers should be of wood, 2 by 4 in., about 30 in. long.

4. Lay the staggered sleepers not more than 12 in. apart on centers. They should be installed at right angles to the finished floor (Figure 151).

5. The sleepers should be lapped at least 3 to 4 in., and more if possible.

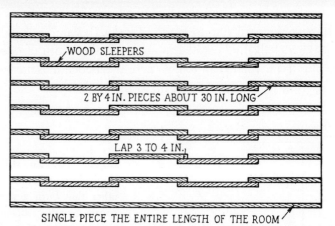

Figure 150. Tongue-and-groove hardwood strip flooring is applied to these staggered sleepers embedded in mastic on top of poured concrete slab subfloor. Flooring is nailed on at right angles to the sleepers.

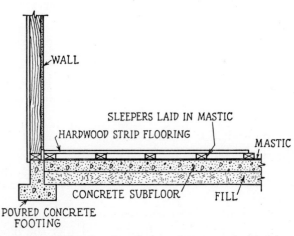

Figure 151. Hardwood flooring installed on sleepers embedded in mastic laid on poured-concrete subfloor.

6. Construction of the strip flooring will be the same as for any other floor as far as cutting, nailing, sanding, etc., is concerned. End joints need not come over the sleepers.

How to install wood-block floors over wood subfloors

1. Clean the subfloor thoroughly and lay down a layer of 15-lb. felt vaporproof paper. Lap the edges at least 3 in.

2. Start at the wall line to lay the blocks.

3. Strike a chalk line parallel to one wall, the width of one block away, plus 1 in. for expansion. Where a baseboard is to be used, measure from it instead of from the wall.

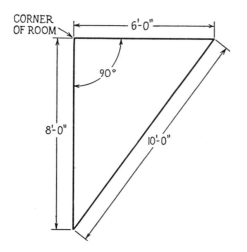

Figure 152. To strike two chalk lines adjacent to each other that form a perfect 90 degree angle, measure off two distances, 6 and 8 ft. each, along adjacent walls. If the angle is square, the diagonal line will be exactly 10 ft. long.

4. Strike a chalk line along the adjacent wall in the same manner, so that the two chalk lines will be at right angles to each other (Figure 152).

5. Start the installation at the corner of the room at the intersections of the two chalk lines.

6. Lay the grooved sides to the wall and the tongue sides to the chalk lines.

7. Face-nail the first block, No. 1, with 4d finish nails.

8. Place the face nails ½ in. from the edge of the block, where they will be covered by the base shoe (Figure 153).

9. Next blind-nail or toenail through the tongue and set the nailheads.

10. Next place blocks 2 and 3. Follow these with blocks 4, 5, and 6 (Figure 154).

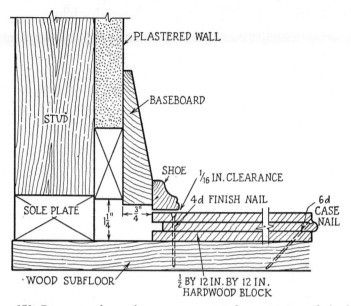

Figure 153. Be sure to leave the necessary space for expansion of the block floors. This should not be less than 1½ in. at each side of the room.

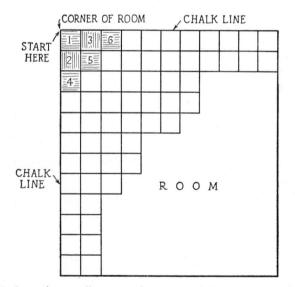

Figure 154. Start the installation at the corner of the room. Lay the grooved sides to the wall and the tongue side to the chalk lines.

11. Continue laying the blocks across the room in this manner to completion.

12. Be sure to leave the necessary expansion at the walls as shown in Figure 153.

How to lay wood-block floors over concrete-slab subfloors

1. The concrete slab must be perfectly dry and should be constructed with proper insulation and vaporproofing, preparatory to this type of floor installation.

2. Prime all concrete subfloors with a standard asphalt priming paint and allow them to dry before starting to lay the blocks.

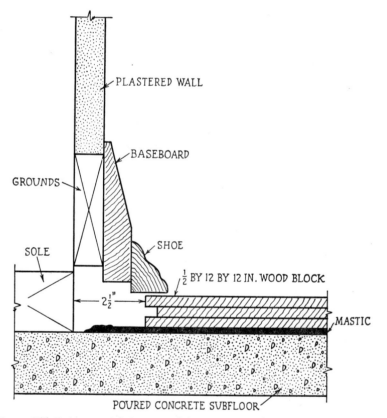

Figure 155. It is essential that a sufficient amount of space be left for the expansion of the wood blocks. For concrete floors, this should never be less than 2½ in., more if possible.

3. Prepare the room for laying the blocks by making a line layout as described in Figure 152.

4. Heat the mastic according to the manufacturer's directions and apply it to the floor.

5. Allow the mastic to set or glaze. Then the blocks can be laid into place.

6. To lay the blocks, tilt them slightly when fitting the tongue and grooves together. This prevents the mastic from grabbing. The blocks will become imbedded thoroughly in a few hours.

7. Start laying the blocks as shown in Figure 154.

8. Start with block 1.

9. Then lay blocks 2, 3, 4, 5, 6, etc., in order.

10. Continue across the room in this manner to completion.

11. It is most necessary to leave the required space for expansion, as shown in Figure 155.

How to estimate hardwood strip flooring

1. Determine the number of square feet of surface in the floor to be covered. Do this by multiplying the length of the room in feet by the width of the room in feet.

Example: A room is 12 by 14 ft. square.
Solution: $12 \times 14 = 168$ sq. ft.

2. Decide on the type of flooring to be used and add the amount of percentage listed in Table 21, page 170.

3. Assuming that we would use oak flooring, size $1\frac{3}{16}$ in. by $2\frac{1}{4}$ in., we would add to the 168 sq. ft., $33\frac{1}{3}$ per cent more, as shown in the table. Thus:

$$\frac{1}{3} \times 168 = 56 \text{ sq. ft.}$$

$$168 + 56 = 224 \text{ sq. ft.,}$$

or the total number of sq. ft. needed.

How to estimate hardwood block flooring

1. Most commonly used oak flooring blocks are 9 in. square. Thus 16 blocks would cover 1 sq. yd., or 9 sq. ft. They are usually packed

32 pieces to a carton. Thus one carton would cover 18 sq. ft., or 2 sq. yd.

2. Determine the number of square feet in the floor to be covered.

3. Do this by multiplying the length of the room in feet by the width of the room in feet.

> *Example:* A room is 12 ft. by 14 ft. square.
> *Solution:* 12 × 14 = 168 sq. ft.
> $$\frac{168}{18} = 9.6 \text{ cartons}$$

As nothing less than full cartons are sold, 10 cartons would be ordered for the floor.

Hardwood block flooring units are made in several sizes from $\frac{1}{2}$ in. to $3\frac{3}{32}$ in. thick and from 6 by 6 to $11\frac{1}{4}$ by $11\frac{1}{4}$ in. sq.

For estimating sizes other than that given above, refer to Table 22.

TABLE 22. UNIT BLOCK SIZES FOR HARDWOOD FLOORING

Strip width, inches	$\frac{1}{2}$ in. thick, inches	$2\frac{5}{32}$ in. thick, inches	$3\frac{3}{32}$ in. thick, inches
$1\frac{1}{2}$	$7\frac{1}{2} \times 7\frac{1}{2}$	$7\frac{1}{2} \times 7\frac{1}{2}$	$7\frac{1}{2} \times 7\frac{1}{2}$
	9×9	9×9	9×9
	6×12	6×12	6×12
2	8×8	8×8	8×8
	10×10	10×10	10×10
	6×12	6×12	6×12
$2\frac{1}{4}$	. . . .	$6\frac{3}{4} \times 6\frac{3}{4}$	$6\frac{3}{4} \times 6\frac{3}{4}$
	. . . .	9×9	9×9
	. . . .	$11\frac{1}{4} \times 11\frac{1}{4}$	$11\frac{1}{4} \times 11\frac{1}{4}$
	. . . .	$6\frac{3}{4} \times 13\frac{1}{2}$	$6\frac{3}{4} \times 13\frac{1}{2}$
$3\frac{1}{4}$	. . . .	$6\frac{1}{2} \times 13$	$6\frac{1}{2} \times 13$

STAIRS AND STEPS

Definition. Stairs can be defined as a series of steps ascending or descending from one floor or level to another. Their purpose is to provide an easy method or means of ascending or descending from one floor to another, the most common method in small-house construction. *Stairs* are usually classified as "open" or "closed" and generally lead from one floor to another. *Steps* may be open or closed and are generally used where very short rises occur, usually at front porches, back porches, landings, terraces, etc.

Sizes. Stair treads and risers vary in size (Figure 156). The size is determined entirely by the rise and run allowed for the stairs or

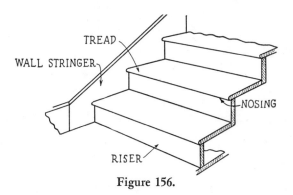

Figure 156.

steps. Where space permits, treads should be from 10 to 12 in. wide and the risers should be 7 to 8 in. high.

How to determine the rise and run. In constructing any stairs or steps, first determine the amount of rise and the amount of run to be used (Figure 157). The *rise* of a flight of stairs is the total perpendicular distance to which the stairs will rise, or the actual distance between the floor levels of the building (Figure 157). This is generally figured from finish floor to finish floor. It is the total sum of all widths of all risers.

The *run* of a flight of stairs is the distance measured on a level from the foot of the stairs to a point directly under the upper end or point of landing (Figure 157). The *nosing* on a tread is the projection over the front edge, usually about the thickness of the treads. The *stringer* is the finish board at the end of the treads against the wall. It forms a protection for the plaster. Stringers or horses are also used under the treads and risers, for support (Figure 158).

In designing stairs, the following rules should be remembered:

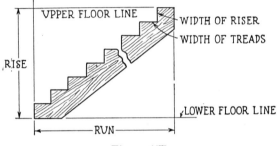

Figure 157.

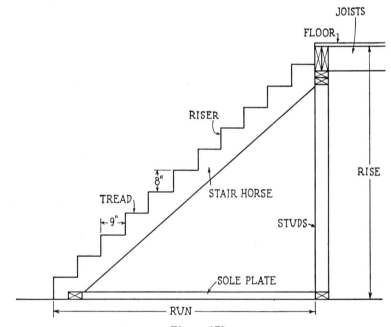

Figure 158.

1. The sum of the rise and run should not be less than 17 in. or more than 18 in.

2. Twice the rise plus the run should not be less than 24 in. or more than 25 in.

3. The result of the rise multiplied by the run should not be less than 70 in. or more than 75 in.

4. Stairs with a rise of $7\frac{1}{2}$ in. and a run of 10 in. are considered very good.

5. In residence work, however, a rise of 8 in. and a run of 10 in. may be used.

6. Little used stairs, such as those to attics, may be built with rises of 8 in. and runs of 8 in.

7. The nosing on the treads should project about $\frac{3}{4}$ in. to $1\frac{1}{2}$ in.

8. In cutting out the stair horse, always deduct the thickness of the tread from the first riser.

9. After the location, size, and type of stairs to be used have been decided upon, the next step is to find the number of risers and treads needed.

How to find the number of risers and treads. First decide on the height of riser desired and the width of tread desired. Variations in

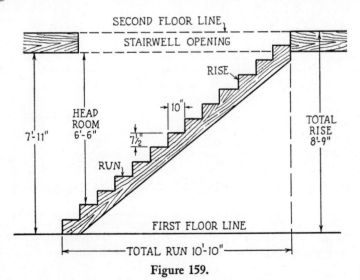

Figure 159.

these sizes may have to be accepted. For example, in Figure 159 the distance between the two floors is found to be 8 ft. 9 in., which is 105 in. As a trial, assume there will be 13 risers; 105 divided by 13 equals $8\frac{1}{13}$. This would make the stairs steep and hard to climb, so divide 105 by 14, which equals $7\frac{1}{2}$ in. By application of the rule —tread plus 2 risers equals 25—a tread with a $7\frac{1}{2}$-in. rise is found to be 10 in.

Since there is always one less tread than there are risers, the horizontal distance, or the run of the stairs, with the $7\frac{1}{2}$-in. rise, would be 130 in., or 10 ft. 10 in.

Headroom is a very important consideration in designing stairs. In all residence and frame-house construction the headroom should never be less than 6 ft. 6 in. (Figure 159).

How to lay out and cut stair horses

1. Mark off a measuring line on which to step off distances.

2. This should be far enough in from the edge to allow the corner of the square to be even with the edge of the horse or to allow a cut with a depth equal to the width of the treads.

3. Mark off spaces on the measuring line as shown in Figure 160.

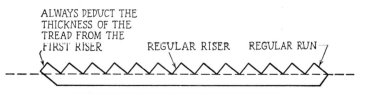

ALWAYS DEDUCT THE THICKNESS OF THE TREAD FROM THE FIRST RISER   REGULAR RISER   REGULAR RUN

MEASURING LINE-NOT ALWAYS THE MIDDLE

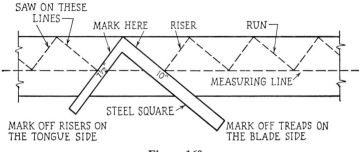

SAW ON THESE LINES   MARK HERE   RISER   RUN

MEASURING LINE

STEEL SQUARE

MARK OFF RISERS ON THE TONGUE SIDE   MARK OFF TREADS ON THE BLADE SIDE

Figure 160.

Use the figure on the tongue to represent the rise and the figure on the blade to represent the run, or tread.

4. There should be the same number of spaces stepped off as there are risers.

5. Cut back the ends at right angles, or square with the risers at the bottom and with the treads at the top.

6. Cut out with a sharp saw, cutting accurately and to the line.

7. Deduct and cut off the thickness of the first tread from the height of the first riser.

Disappearing stairways. Disappearing stairways are usually obtainable in ready-built and assembled units, ready to be installed by the carpenter. They provide an easy access to the attic and take up no floor space. However, they are usually of very light construction and are built steep, with narrow treads. They are used a great deal in basementless houses, where added storage space is needed.

There are many sizes. They range from 7 ft. 6 in. to 10 ft. in height in standard stock, but can be obtained in any size by being specially built.

They are installed as a unit in an opening cut into and between the ceiling joists. They are usually installed in the ceiling in a hall or a utility room, for easy access. The opening should be cased with the same trim as the rest of the woodwork in the house.

OUTSIDE FINISH OR TRIM

Outside finish is the term applied to those parts of the outside of a house that generally go to make up the trim. It includes:

1. Frieze boards
2. Fascia boards
3. Plancier boards
4. Molds
5. Corner boards
6. Shutters
7. Wood steps
8. Wood posts
9. Window casings
10. Door casings
11. Garage doors
12. Window boxes
13. Screens, etc.

Outside trim is generally classified as all other than the main wall coverings. All outside trim is usually of white pine or cypress and should be primed when nailed or set into place.

ROOF CORNICES

Definition. A cornice is that part of house construction where the roof and side walls intersect (Figure 161). Its purpose is to provide a definite and satisfactory finish at this point. The size is determined largely by the size of the house and the type of architecture.

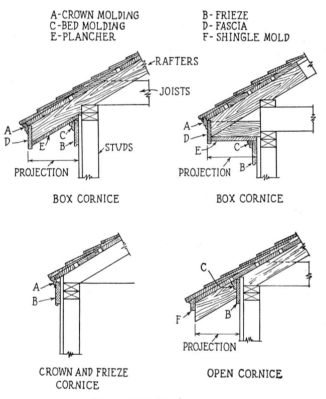

Figure 161. Roof cornices.

Types of cornice. It would be difficult to explain all the different types of cornice here, but in general, the main purpose of the construction is to conceal the ends of the rafters and at the same time provide a pleasing finish around the roof at its intersection with the side walls.

Crown and frieze cornice, used on
  1. Cape Cod style
  2. Colonial style
  3. Adaptations
  4. Inexpensive construction

Open cornice, used on
  1. Bungalows
  2. Summer cottages
  3. Sleeping porches
  4. Garages
  5. Rustic construction

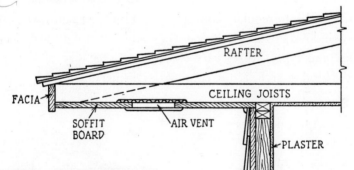

Figure 162. Modern ranch-type architecture employs the use of the extremely wide overhang. This projection requires the use of a soffit. Where these overhang widths are 12 in. or less, they are usually called "plancher boards."

Box cornice, used on
1. Colonial types
2. Early American types
3. Modern types

The frieze, fascia, plancier board, crown mold, bed mold, and shingle mold are usually white pine or cypress and should be primed as soon as they are nailed or set in place.

Cornice construction on the modern ranch-style architecture makes use of the extremely wide overhang, and this is used also in other types of houses designed with solar orientation principles. These overhangs, however, should be designed whenever possible with the professional advice of an architect. This type of cornice is shown in Figure 162.

DORMER WINDOWS

Definition. A dormer window is a window framed out from the roof (Figure 163). The purpose is to enable attic space to be transformed into regular room space by admitting light. Sometimes these windows are above the eave line and sometimes below.

Sizes and types. Sizes vary according to the size of the house and the kind of architecture employed. Dormers may be classified as follows:

1. Flat-top dormers
2. Gable dormers
3. Hip dormers

Construction. When the roof is being framed for a dormer window, an opening must be left and the dormer built into this opening (Figure 164). The spans are usually short, and therefore light material may be used.

Occasionally the rafters on either side of the opening are doubled. Of course, headers must be used. It is not uncommon for dormers to be framed by 2 by 4's or even 2 by 3's in roofs where 2 by 8's or

2 by 10's have been used for rafters. Where it is necessary to determine sizes, the same principles that were explained in the discus-

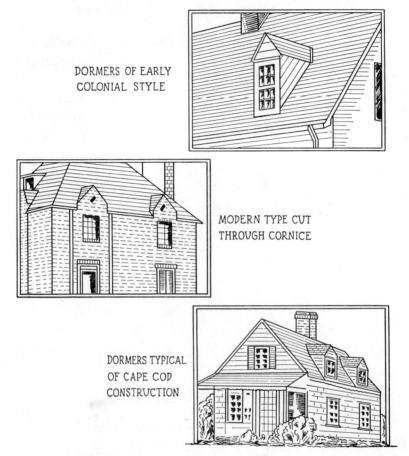

DORMERS OF EARLY
COLONIAL STYLE

MODERN TYPE CUT
THROUGH CORNICE

DORMERS TYPICAL
OF CAPE COD
CONSTRUCTION

Figure 163. Dormer windows.

sion on rafters and joists can be applied. The framing should be
nailed with 8*d* and 16*d* common nails. Necessary sizes for the window openings and the sash are usually shown on the plans or provided by the architect.

A dormer framing assembly is shown in Figure 165.

Figure 164. When framing the roof for a dormer, an opening must be left and the dormer built into it.

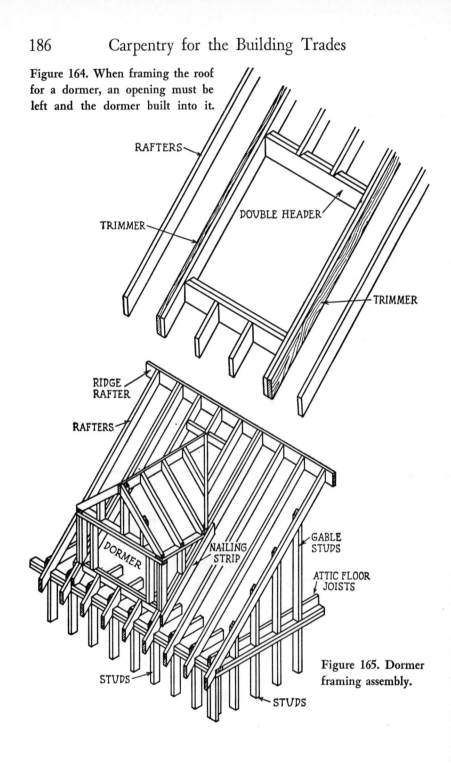

RAFTERS

TRIMMER

DOUBLE HEADER

TRIMMER

RIDGE RAFTER

RAFTERS

DORMER

NAILING STRIP

GABLE STUDS

ATTIC FLOOR JOISTS

STUDS

STUDS

Figure 165. Dormer framing assembly.

WINDOWS AND WINDOW FRAMES

Modern design has taken hold of windows as well as of other parts of the house, making them architectural features rather than just necessary openings in a wall to admit light and air. The majority of today's designs have as their focal point a picture window.

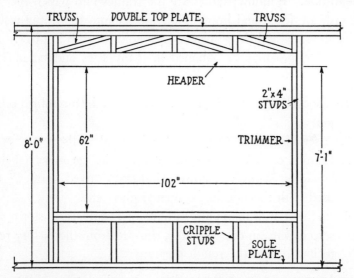

Figure 166. A rough opening for a 24 by 26 triple window. A double header should be used at the top, and, in cases of wide openings, the openings should be trussed. When studding is cut away, strength of the wall is lost. This strength must be replaced by doubling the studs on each side of the opening.

Glass areas have increased and the proportions of glass within the frames have increased. Windows have changed in shape. The high, narrow window is no longer standard. Windows tend to be much wider, with individual sash divided into horizontal panels.

Windows are better built than they were and, since they are, it is more important than ever that they be properly installed. Flashing at the top of the frames and at the sills is just as important as flashing on the roof. If possible, calking material should be injected all around the edges of the window frames where they fit into framing or against masonry.

Also, good construction around window frames is essential to good building. Where frames are to be set, studding must be cut away and its equivalent strength replaced by doubling the studs on each side of the opening. A double header should be used at the top and, in the case of a wide opening, the opening should be trussed (Figure 166).

Definition. Window frames are the frames into which the window sash are fitted and hung. They are set into the frame wall to receive the sash, and their purpose is to hold the sash in place.

Sizes. Frames may be obtained in many sizes and types. They are usually in the following forms:

1. Knocked-down sections, factory built, to be assembled on the job
2. Assembled frames constructed at local mills
3. Frames constructed on the job by the carpenter, such as "window walls," "picture windows," "fixed frames," etc., used with thermopane, insulated glass, etc.
4. Prefitted and preassembled units of frames, sash, storm sash, screens, etc., in one assembly, shipped from the factory ready to install into the rough opening

Window frames may be secured in either single or multiple sizes. They may be for stationary, double-hung check rail, casements, fixed sash, window wall, awning-type sash, and many others.

Double-hung windows are usually fitted with weights, pulleys, overhead balances, springs, pressure plates, or other forms of lifts. Some types have subcasings outside that are nailed directly to the studs. In others, the outside casing is nailed over the sheathing. The type of frame used will of course determine the type of installation needed.

How to set window frames

1. Check the rough opening and see that it is made at least 10 in. larger each way than the window-glass size of the sash to be used.

> *Example:* If the sash to be used is a two-light window, 24 by 26, we would add 10 in. to 24 for a total of 34 in. for the width of

the rough opening. We would then add the upper and lower glass, 26 in. each, plus 10 in. for a total of 62 in. or the height of the rough opening. Thus the rough opening would be 34 in. wide and 62 in. high. This allowance is standard and provides for weights, springs, balances, room for plumbing and squaring, and regular adjustments.

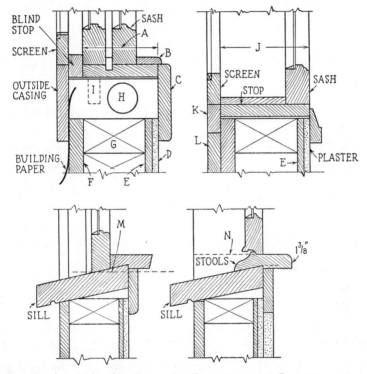

Figure 167. *A*, width of pulley style; *B*, inside stop; *C*, inside casing; *D*, plaster; *E*, lath; *F*, siding; *G*, studs; *H*, weight; *I*, optional sash balance; *J*, width of casement jamb; *K*, outside casing; *L*, siding; *M*, double-hung frame measured from here; *N*, casement frames measured from here.

2. Tack a strip of heavy building paper, about 12 in. wide, all around the outside of the opening, over the sheathing (Figures 167 and 168).

3. Set the frame in place, allowing the subsill to rest on the rough frame at the bottom.

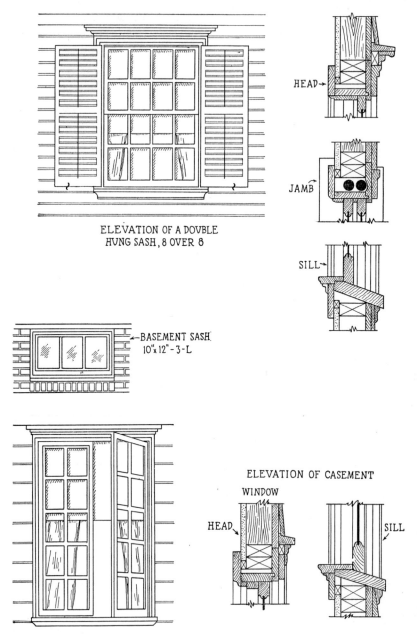

ELEVATION OF A DOUBLE
HUNG SASH, 8 OVER 8

HEAD→

JAMB

SILL→

←BASEMENT SASH
10"x 12" - 3 - L

ELEVATION OF CASEMENT
WINDOW

HEAD

SILL

Figure 168.

4. Adjust the top of the frame to the required height. All doors and windows should be the same height, both rough and finished. They are usually 6 ft. 8 in. from the finished floor to the underside of the head jamb of the door and the head jamb of the window frame.

5. If wedging is necessary in order to level, use shingles or laths. This, however, should be only temporary, or until the frame is nailed into place.

6. Level the subsill and hold the frame in place.

7. Put one nail through the outside casing or subcasing into the sheathing or studs at the lower corners.

8. Plumb the two side casings and nail them onto the wall from the outside.

9. Use 8d common nails and do not set.

PICTURE WINDOWS AND FRAMES

Modern developments in fenestration have brought into wide usage the type of window known as the "picture window." A picture window does not necessarily mean a large expanse of glass. It may consist of a well-arranged group of manufactured window units or can be a glazed opening tempered with muntins.

Most picture-window frames are equipped with double-glass units, often called "air-blanket insulated glass." Such a unit consists of two pieces of good-quality crystal or plate glass with a hermetically sealed air space between them. The insulating qualities of this air space, which is usually $\frac{1}{4}$ in. or $\frac{1}{2}$ in., reduce condensation, which occurs on large glass areas in the colder climates. They also reduce greatly the heat loss and the transmission of noise.

Installation of glass of this type does not require any special equipment or knowledge. Glazing instructions are usually sent along with the glass from the manufacturer. Storm sash need not be used when double insulated glass is installed.

While these doubled-paned units are the most logical solution for picture windows and window walls of glass in colder climates, ordinary plate glass or crystal will achieve the same effect in areas where cold weather is no problem.

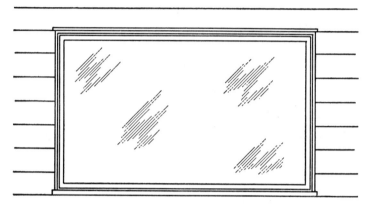

Figure 169. A fixed window without the flanking units.

Definition. Most picture windows and frames fall into one of *three* groups:

1. A fixed window without flanking units (Figure 169).
2. Standard units with flanking units. These may be casement or double-hung windows (Figure 170).
3. Window walls. These may be fixed or with ventilating units. They are usually of ceiling height (Figure 171).

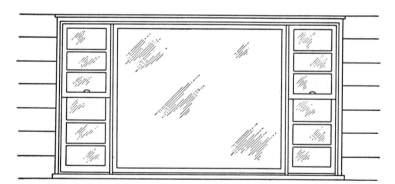

Figure 170. A picture window with a fixed center section of insulated glass and double-hung flanking units.

Sizes. Fixed picture windows and frames and standard unit frames are obtainable at most lumberyards and may be fitted with

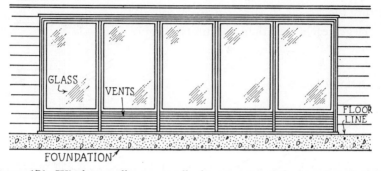

Figure 171. Window walls are usually large sections of glassed walls, with fixed sections above, and with ventilators below. Window walls are usually made floor-to-ceiling height.

or without insulated glass. They come in many sizes for both the center fixed glass and the side units. Lists of sizes for both frames and sash, giving also the rough opening needed for each, are available from either the dealer or the manufacturer.

Construction. Excellent results are obtained when building window walls or frames for extra-large glass areas by using dressed 2- by 6-in. stock framing material for the basic unit. These units may be floor-to-ceiling height or may be broken up by the use of muntins of the same materials (Figure 172). Not only would these muntins temper the light entering the house, but the heavy bars may be effectively used to accentuate the horizontal or vertical lines of the building.

How to install picture-window frames

1. Determine the size of window to be used.

2. Determine the number of sashes and the size of each needed, or the number and size of the insulated units to be used.

3. Make a simple frame of dressed lumber, with or without muntins as the design calls for.

4. Use 2- by 6-in. pieces for the head, jambs, sills, and muntins (Figure 173).

5. Rout out the sill and the head for the installation of drip caps.

6. The inside dimensions of the frame should be ½ in. larger than the size of the insulated glass units. This allows for the mastic, setting blocks, etc. If spacer strips are used, the frame should be 1⅛ in. larger each way than the units (Figure 172).

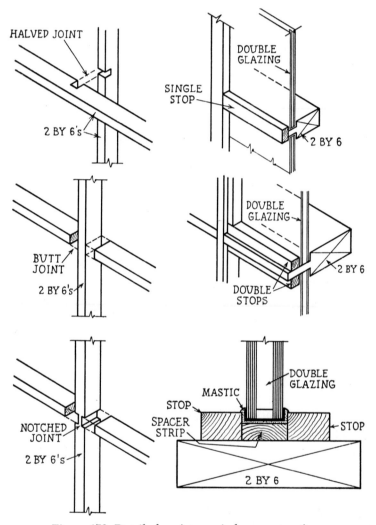

Figure 172. Details for picture-window construction.

7. Make the frame square and plumb.

8. Install the frame into the rough opening. See that it is level, plumb, and true.

9. Nail the frame in place with 8d case nails. If spacer strips are to be used, cut and nail them into place.

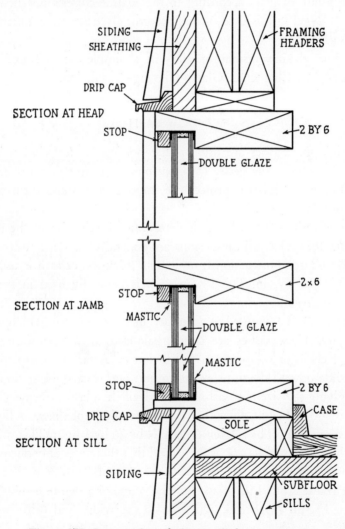

Figure 173. Cross section of picture-window construction.

10. Cut and install all stop. If inside stop is to be used, nail it on first and permanently.

11. The outside stop should be cut, fitted, and nailed into place temporarily until the glass or the sash is set or hung, whichever is used.

12. Install all glass according to the manufacturer's instructions.

13. If wood sash is used, install accordingly. (See section on window sash.)

14. For glazing insulating glass in a simple wood frame, see "Glazing" in Chapter 6, Glass—Glazing—Insulation.

WINDOW SASH

Definition. Sashes are usually that portion of the window that holds or contains the glass. Their purpose is to provide an opening to admit light and still protect the interior of a house from cold, heat, dust, wind, etc.

Size of sash. The sash size is determined by the size of the glass (Figure 167). Over-all dimensions are generally standard and made to fit standard construction frames. The thickness of sash is usually $1\frac{1}{8}$, $1\frac{3}{8}$, or $1\frac{3}{4}$ in. The $1\frac{3}{8}$-in. sash is generally used in frame-house construction.

A window is composed of an upper and a lower sash, which slide vertically. These sashes are counterbalanced by weights hung on cord or chain or by means of sash balances. A sash is one piece. It may slide up and down or swing in and out, or may be stationary.

In giving the size of a sash, the width of the glass is always given first, then the height, then the number of pieces of glass, or lights. Thus a sash might be spoken of as a 24 by 26 by 1 light. This means that the glass itself was 24 by 26 in. and that there was only one piece of glass. However, the sash would be larger than 24 by 26 in. because of the frame around the glass. For the frame of a two-light window with a $1\frac{3}{8}$-in. check rail, add 4 in. to the width and 6 in. to the length.

Example: A two-light window has a glass size of 24 by 26, meaning that the glass in each sash is 24 in. wide and 26 in. high.
Find the size of the window frame.

Solution: 24 + 4 = 28, or 2 ft. 4 in., the width. 26 × 2 = 52,
or 52 in. 52 + 6 = 58, or 4 ft. 10 in., the length.

Therefore, the window-frame size for these sashes would be 2 ft.
4 in. by 4 ft. 10 in. D.H., or double hung.

Types of sash. There are two general types of wood sash: (1)
fixed or permanent, (2) movable.

Fixed sash are removable only with the aid of a carpenter.

Movable sash may be of the variety that slide up and down in
channels in the frame, or of the casement type that swing in or out
and are hinged at the side. Sliding sash are counterbalanced by
weights, called "sash weights," their actual weight being equal to
one-half that of each sash. For example, if a window sash weighs
12 lb., it would require two 6-lb. weights to counterbalance it. These
weights are hung in the frame by sash cords passing over a pulley
in the frame and attached to the side of the sash.

Other types are spring balances attached at the top of the frame
and supporting the sash by long steel ribbons secured to the side of
the sash.

Sash are classified according to the number of lights: single or
divided. Divided sash may have an indefinite number of patterns,
usually determined by the kind of architecture (Figure 174).

Perhaps nowhere else is the most careful workmanship so essential as in the fitting of window sash. They must be properly fitted
and carefully balanced. Weights that are too light will allow a sash
to fall; those too heavy will prevent it from properly seating. Im-
proper balance causes broken glass. If the sash are fitted too loosely,
they develop rattle and permit dust, air, and moisture to filter in
around them; if *too tightly,* they are an endless source of trouble
in raising and lowering. Whenever possible, a good grade of metal
weather strip should be used on all movable sash. A great many

manufacturers are now producing a frame, sash, and weather strip, all in one combination. These are set into the frame wall in one unit and are proving very satisfactory as far as good construction and operation are concerned.

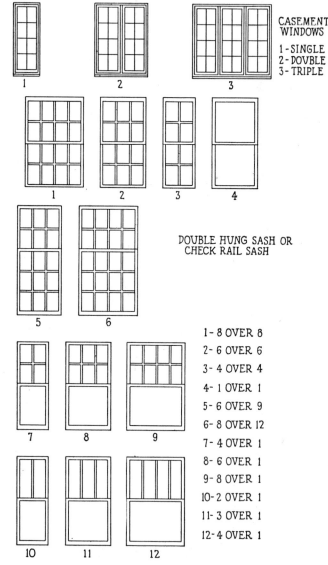

CASEMENT
WINDOWS

1 - SINGLE
2 - DOVBLE
3 - TRIPLE

DOUBLE HUNG SASH OR
CHECK RAIL SASH

1- 8 OVER 8
2- 6 OVER 6
3- 4 OVER 4
4- 1 OVER 1
5- 6 OVER 9
6- 8 OVER 12
7- 4 OVER 1
8- 6 OVER 1
9- 8 OVER 1
10- 2 OVER 1
11- 3 OVER 1
12- 4 OVER 1

Figure 174. Divided sash.

How to fit a double-hung wood sash

1. Prepare the sash cords, chains, or balances that are to be used. If cords are used, tie them to the weights, run them through the pulleys at the top, and tie a knot in the end of each. This knot will be set in the side of the sash in a recess made to receive it.

2. The length of the cord can be determined by placing the sash in its position and measuring. When the inside sash is down in place, the weight for that sash should be near the top pulley. When the outside sash is up in place, the weight for it should be down, not quite touching the bottom.

3. Fit the outside top sash first.

4. Do not fit it too tightly, allow for swelling.

5. Use a sharp plane for squaring.

6. Remove the parting bead on one side of the frame to enable you to put the sash into place. This is the strip about ½ by ¾ in. which is grooved into the frame on each side, separating the two sash.

7. Notch out each end of the check rail as far as the parting bead extends beyond the frame. This should be done very accurately to prevent bad fitting, which in turn would either let in wind and cold or, if too tight, cause the sash to slide hard (Figure 175).

8. When the sash is fitted, put it in place, replace the parting beads, and attach sash cords to the sides.

9. Plane and fit the inside bottom sash next for easy operation.

10. Fit the sides of it first.

11. After the sides have been fitted, set the sash in place and determine how much, if any, need come off the bottom other than the bevel that is always planed on to match the slant of the window sill (Figure 168).

12. The two check rails must come together and be even at the middle of the window. If not, the window locks will not meet or be workable.

13. If the rails do not match, scribe off the necessary amount at the bottom, taking care to keep the same bevel on the bottom edge of the sash.

14. When the lower sash is fitted, put it in place, secure the sash cords, and check both sash for easy operation.

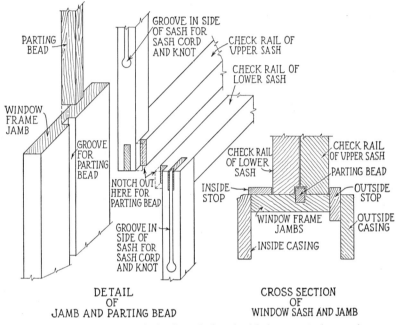

DETAIL
OF
JAMB AND PARTING BEAD

CROSS SECTION
OF
WINDOW SASH AND JAMB

Figure 175. Details of check rails for double-hung window sash.

DOORS

Definition. Doors are the shutters for doorways. Their purpose is to provide a means of closing or shutting off one room, compartment, or area from another. There are various types as follows:

1. Interior doors, used inside buildings
2. Exterior doors, used at outside entrances
3. French doors, used inside or outside
4. Sliding doors
5. Folding doors
6. Cabinet doors, for cases, cupboards, etc.

Interior doors may be constructed in several ways. There are *four* general types as follows:

1. Panel doors
2. Flush doors
3. French doors
4. Louver doors, sometimes called "shutter doors"

All are very popular, each contributing its own part to its own type of architecture. Modern-type architecture is making special use of

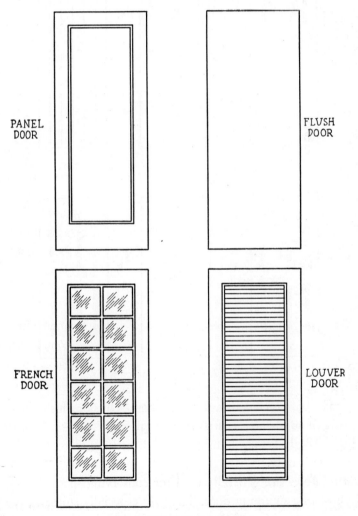

Figure 176. Interior doors.

the flush door and the louver door. The louver door is used a great deal in ranch-style architecture. The four general types of doors are shown in Figure 176.

Exterior doors and their patterns are usually chosen to correspond to certain types of architecture. They may be with or without glass.

Figure 177. Exterior-door patterns.

They may be panel doors or flush doors. Outside flush doors are generally of solid-core construction (Figure 177). *French doors* are used where light is to be admitted, and sometimes merely for decorative purposes only.

Sliding doors are generally used for conserving space that is normally lost to a swinging door. They are especially suited for closets in bedrooms, etc. Most sliding-door installations involve job-building, with manufacturers supplying only the tracks and the hardware. In some cases the tracks may be of wood. Usually, metal-sill guides are furnished for smooth guidance of the door bottom, but this is

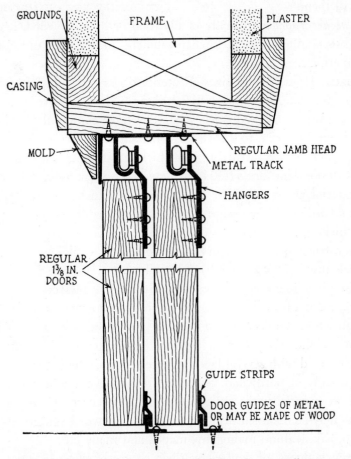

Figure 178. Typical cross section of sliding-door installation.

sometimes accomplished by means of a hardwood scuffing strip (Figure 178). Double doors that slide past each other lend themselves readily to installation in various types of cabinets and built-ins, especially kitchen cabinets. Some manufacturers build a complete prefabricated frame, with or without the doors, that may be installed into the stud walls during the construction.

The *folding door,* a new type of fabric-covered folding frame, is also popular. These doors are easy to install and take up little space. As is the case with other doors, it is the duty of the carpenter to install them.

Cabinet doors are usually of plywood or of solid wood, and are used on storage cabinets, kitchen cabinets, linen closets, utility-room cabinets, etc.

Sizes. Regular stock sizes of interior doors run from 2 ft. 6 in. to 3 ft. 6 in. wide, and from 6 to 7 ft. long. Other sizes are obtainable but are not considered stock sizes. The most commonly used sizes are from 2 ft. 6 in. to 2 ft. 8 in. wide, and 6 ft. to 6 ft. 8 in. long. Interior doors are usually 1⅜ in. thick. Most commonly used sizes for exterior doors are 3 ft. 0 in. wide and 6 ft. 8 in. long. All outside, or exterior, doors should be 1¾ in. thick. Cabinet doors will vary in size according to the design used, but are generally $1\frac{3}{16}$ in. to 1⅛ in. thick.

Construction. Panel doors are those that have stiles and rails with panels inserted (Figure 179). The stiles and rails may be of fir or white pine. The panels may be of any kind of plywood of various thicknesses. Flush doors may be of either solid-core or hollow-core construction. Hollow-core doors are very popular because of their light weight. They have a built-up hollow, cross-grid-constructed core covered with several layers of face veneers. Their stiles and rails are usually of hardwood. Solid-core doors have a solid wood core and are covered with several layers of face veneers. Doors of both types may be obtained in many kinds of hardwood veneers, such as birch, oak, walnut, mahogany, maple, and many others.

French doors, of course, by their nature of construction are of solid wood. They may be made of any hardwood or softwood.

Grades. Doors are usually divided into four grades for quality: No. 1, No. 2, No. 3, and No. 4. Numbers 1 and 2 are most commonly used.

How to fit and hang doors. The parts of a door are the stiles, rails, and panels (Figure 179). Sometimes panels are replaced by glass panes.

1. From the blueprint determine whether the door swings to the right or the left.

2. Mark around with a square and saw off the lugs (Figure 179).

3. Hold the door to place and check for size and squareness.

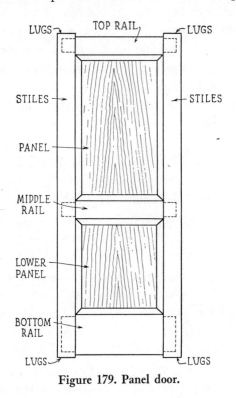

Figure 179. Panel door.

4. Plane one edge of the door until it fits the frame or jamb on the side it is to be hung.

5. Plane the top edge until it fits the head of the jamb.

6. Hold the door in place against the fitted edge and fitted top and scribe the other edge from the inside of the other jamb.

7. The exact length of door need not be determined until after it is hung and the finish floors are laid. After this is done, scribe the bottom with the floor and mark the allowance of about ½ in.

8. Cut off and plane down the bottom of the door.

A door should be fitted with about ⅛ in. of space or "play" all around it. This, however, should be uniform and even. The free edge of the door will need to be planed somewhat lower at the back arris than at the front, to prevent the door from rubbing as it is opened.

How to hinge a door

1. Place the door in position against the door stops.

2. Be sure to have proper allowance around the door.

3. Block it in place temporarily.

4. Measure down from the top and up from the bottom to locate the hinges.

5. Mark these points with a sharp knife. (The top hinge is usually set down 7 in.; bottom hinge, set up 11 in.)

6. Remove the door and chisel out gains on the frame and the door, if the hinges are loose butts. If it is a half-surface hinge, gain only on the jamb (Figure 180).

7. Screw the hinges in place on the jamb and on the door, if they are loose butts (Figure 180).

8. If a half-surface hinge is used, screw it in place on the jamb and then place the door in position, block it, and screw onto the door the surface half of the hinge.

Locks are usually mortised in. The type of lock will generally suggest the method of installation.

Hand of butt hinges. The hand of a butt hinge is determined from the outside of the door opening to which the door is applied. The outside of a closet door is the room side. If when you are standing *outside,* the door opens from you to the right, it takes right-hand butt hinges; if to the left, left-hand butt hinges. If when you are standing *outside,* the door opens toward you to the right, it takes left-hand butt hinges; if to the left, right-hand butt hinges.

How to handle and care for doors

1. Always store doors in a flat position.

2. Do not have doors brought onto the job until the plaster has dried thoroughly.

3. If the doors are to be primed or stained, this should be done before they are fitted and hung.

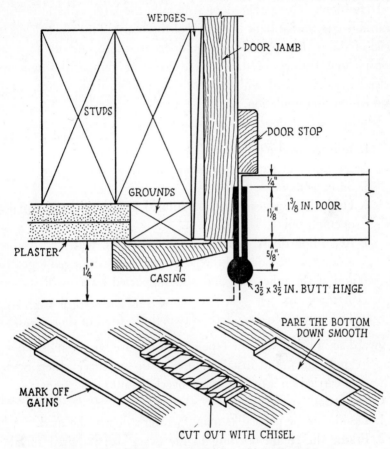

Figure 180. Application of 3½ by 3½ in. butt hinges.

4. If the doors are to be finished natural, take care not to scar, scratch, or discolor the surface in any manner.

5. If the grain of the door is figured, match it with the other doors or woodwork as much as possible.

6. If the doors are flush doors with veneer faces, do not drag them on the corners, as this will break and tear loose the veneer.

GARAGE DOORS

Definition. The garage door is usually the largest single unit of movable equipment built in as part of the house. This is particularly true of the popular double garage door. It is also one of the most conspicuous features of the average house or garage. It should be selected and installed with much thought as to design, size, kind, and ease of manipulation.

Kinds. Garage doors can be classified into six major types:

1. Roll-up sectional, usually 3 or more sections
2. Swing-up or panel type, usually in one section
3. Sliding doors
4. Hinged doors, each section hinged at the side and usually opening out
5. Accordion doors, usually in three sections, with one section hinged at the side and the other two sections hinged together and at the other side and also supported by a small section of track
6. The upward-folding door of two, three, four, or more sections

Upward-acting doors of one type or another are far the most popular, are not difficult to install, and take up no space when open. They are carried on a track up and overhead into the garage.

Construction

1. Decide on the particular manufacturer's door to be used.

2. Frame the rough opening to the exact size required for the finished job. These dimensions are usually sent with the door.

3. Follow the manufacturer's directions rigidly, both in setting the doors and in installing the hardware.

6

GLASS—GLAZING—
INSULATION

GLASS

Glass is a transparent material used in window sash to admit light and still provide protection to the interior of a house from cold, heat, dust, etc. It has recently become widely used for decoration purposes in various types of architecture. Regular stock sizes vary in inches from 6 to 16 in.; above this by even inches up to 60 in. in width and 70 in. in height for double strength, 34 by 50 in. for single strength.

Grades of glass. Glass comes in three grades: (1) single strength, (2) double strength, (3) plate. *Single-strength* glass may be as thin as $\frac{1}{16}$ in., and vary in thickness up to $\frac{1}{8}$ in. *Double-strength* glass will run almost uniformly $\frac{1}{8}$ in. thick. *Plate* glass is the highest grade of window glass, being cast in large sheets on a flat table and then polished. It will vary in thickness from $\frac{1}{4}$ to $\frac{5}{16}$ in.

Both single- and double-strength glass are sorted into three qualities, the classification depending upon color, brilliancy, and flaws:

"AA," the best quality
"A," the second quality
"B," the third quality

"A" and "B" are most commonly used for house construction.

Manufacture of glass. Glass is made by fusing under intense heat a mixture of soda, lime, and sand. For blown glass the ingredients are melted together in vats in huge furnaces. When the mass is ready, it is blown either by men or by machinery into large cylinders of the desired thickness. It is then opened and flattened by heating, and finally inspected and cut into the desired sizes.

GLAZING

How to glaze a sash. Placing glass in a sash is called "glazing." To glaze a window, remove and place the sash on a table or bench with the rabbet side up. If a broken glass is being replaced, the old putty and glass should be removed. *Clean* out all the old putty and glazier points. The rabbet will probably be found to be dry and hard. If it is, prime it with linseed oil or thin paint and let this soak in well. That will cause the putty to adhere more readily and prevent the dry frame from drawing all the oil out of the putty. Next, place the pane of glass in the opening. If the glass needs to be cut, proceed as follows:

1. Measure the glass.
2. Plan it ⅛ in. smaller than the opening.
3. Lay a straightedge on the glass and hold it firmly in place.
4. Hold the cutter firmly against the straightedge and start to cut at the farther edge.
5. Draw the cutter toward you in a firm rapid motion with even pressure.
6. Place the line made by the cutter over the edge of a table top or bench.
7. Press down gently on the projection.

8. If the glass does not break readily, tap the underside gently with the cutter and try again.

After the pane has been cut, place it in the opening and proceed to glaze. Press glazier points into the frame to hold the pane in place and apply the putty, feeding it down under the putty knife as it is drawn along. Putty is composed of whiting, white lead, and linseed oil. If left in the open, it will become hard. Putty should be kept in a closed container and kept covered with a thin skim of linseed oil.

How to install double glazed units

1. Check the opening for the sash to see that it is square and that it has full unit edge clearance.

2. Setting blocks should be located in from each corner and centered to a distance of $\frac{1}{4}$ the length of the glass or sash (Figure 181).

3. Units constructed with one light of heat-absorbing plate must be glazed with the heat-absorbing glass to the outside.

4. Double-glass units must have a sufficient bed of glazing compound so that neither the wood nor the metal will come in contact with the glass at any point.

5. Use a good grade of glazing compound. It must be free of corrosive materials.

6. Have the glazing compound soft, and completely bed the sash with it before inserting the unit.

7. Press the glass unit into place gently. Press it in evenly, do not force it or twist it.

8. Do not nip the corners for any purpose. By doing this you may break the seal.

9. Set the unit so that there will be equal clearance all around it.

10. Point up all voids along the edges between the sash and the glass.

11. If wood stops are used without rabbets in the sash, do not use undue pressure in placing them as it will squeeze out too much of the compound and allow the wood to touch the glass unit (Figure 181).

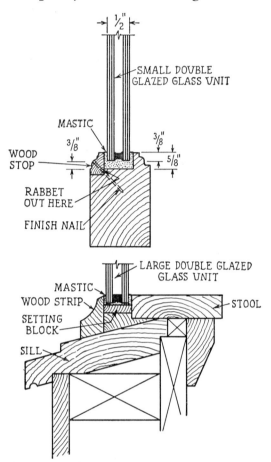

Figure 181. Lights over 80 united inches (a united inch, or united inches, equals the total length plus the total width of the glass) must be supported on setting blocks. These blocks may be of hardwood (rot proofed) or of lead.

INSULATION

Definition. Most of the homes built are fully insulated. It has been found that insulation cuts fuel costs so much that it pays for itself in a few years. It also has a hot-weather function, in as much as it slows down the passage of heat into the house from the outside. This, of course, makes for more comfortable living in the summer.

Insulation materials take on many forms. They may be of various materials, such as cotton, rock wool, wood fiber, glass wool, and vermiculite. It is made up into many forms, such as short bats, long bats, rolls, loose fill, pellets, and rigid board.

The primary purpose of insulation is to retard the passage of heat, either from the inside out or from the outside into a house or structure. Heat is a form of energy. It always travels from a warm surface to a cooler one. Heat travels three ways: (1) by conduction, (2) by convection, and (3) by radiation.

Heat passing through solid materials, such as steel and concrete, travels by *conduction.* Through dense materials such as these heat will be conducted much more rapidly than it will through materials which may be permeated by tiny air cells.

When heat travels by way of air currents, it is said to travel by *convection.* When air contacts a cold wall or windowpane it tends to settle as it cools. On the other hand, when air contacts a warm or hot surface it tends to rise as it warms. These reactions set up a continuous circulation, which moves air across space.

When heat flows in a direct line from a source supplying heat units to a cooler surface it is called *radiation.* Sun heat is radiated heat. Heat moving from a person's body to a nearby colder surface, such as a wall or a ceiling, is radiated heat. This radiated heat is then absorbed by the wall or the ceiling which it reaches in proportion to that wall or ceiling's affinity to absorb this heat. This amount, of course, depends on the type of material used in wall or ceiling and the type of construction employed.

The purpose of insulation, then, is very plain, merely to keep these walls, ceilings, floors, etc., as resistant to the escape of heat as possible.

The transfer of heat, or heat loss through building materials, takes place almost entirely by *conduction.* However, heat loss may occur by any or all three of the methods described. Whatever the type of heat loss that takes place, it is well to remember that heat always moves from the *warm side* to the *cold side.*

Types of insulating materials. There are many types of insulating materials on the market. In all of them the fundamental principle is the same. In each, the insulation value is due to the small dead air cells, either within or between the fibers or particles of the materials. The relative insulating value of each is dependent, therefore, on the density of the materials. These insulating materials may be divided into four groups or types: (1) rigid, (2) fill, (3) reflective, and (4) flexible.

RIGID INSULATION

Definition. Rigid insulation is made from wood or other fibers which are compressed into a variety of board forms for sheathing, plaster base, interior finish, and other general insulating purposes. The outstanding characteristics of insulating wallboards are strength, stiffness, finishing possibilities, and insulating values.

Insulating boards in general use are known as building board, sheathing, lath board, tile board, plank and roof insulation, etc.

How to apply rigid insulation. Rigid insulation is usually installed directly onto the studs, ceiling joists, rafters, or elsewhere, depending on the nature of the work. Wherever nailing is exposed, the nails should be set and filled with filler provided for this by the manufacturer. Some insulating board is so constructed that concealed nailing may be done. In this case, it is well to use rustproof nails with flat heads. The flat heads will prevent the material from pulling off or coming loose.

FILL INSULATION

Definition. Fill insulations may be of granulated, shredded, or powdered material. Products used for their manufacture are usually of vegetable, animal, or mineral origin. Fill insulations are usually obtainable in the bulk, being sold in sacks or containers, or by the pound. There are three general types: (1) wood fiber, (2) mineral wools, (3) animal hair.

Wood-fiber wool fill includes several insulations made from the fiber of wood or other vegetable materials. *Mineral wools* include such materials known as rock wool, slag wool, glass wool, etc. *Animal-hair* fill insulation, as the name implies, comes from cattle.

Figure 182. Insulation in the home. This modern method of installing insulation in a home after it has been built is very good and is being used a great deal. In new-home constructon, the insulation is usually built in.

How to apply fill insulation. The application of fill insulations is fairly simple. The material is poured from the bags or containers in which it is sold and is placed by hand between the framing members of the house where it is to be used. In existing walls the insulation may be blown in between the framing members with a blowing machine (Figure 182). Loose-fill insulation of the granulated type may be poured into place and leveled off to the desired thickness.

REFLECTIVE INSULATION

Definition. Reflective insulation consists of thin sheets of bright metal. It operates on an entirely different principle from that of other insulations. This type is effective because it reflects heat; therefore, its efficiency is dependent entirely upon its bright, shiny surface. The insulation value is achieved only when this material faces an air space of at least ¾ in. or more.

The principal types of reflective insulations are: (1) aluminum foil, which may be plain or may be attached to one or both sides of light paper; two or three sheets pleated and made to expand with air pockets formed; (2) aluminum foil attached to one side of gypsum board; (3) paper, faced on one or both sides with aluminum powder; (4) blanket-type insulation, in which one side of the blanket is faced with aluminum foil.

How to install reflective insulation. Reflective insulations are made to be installed either between the framing members, such as the ceiling joists or studs, or with the nailing surfaces brought over the inside edges of the framing members and the reflective surface set in between the members. Regardless of where it is used or how it is installed, the minimum air space of ¾ in. must always be maintained to obtain the maximum efficiency. Wherever possible, it is well to divide the air space into two separate air spaces with the reflective insulation. This will increase the value of the insulation, provided that there are no openings left for the passage of air between the two air spaces. Reflective insulation material is usually applied with staples. When foil-backed gypsum board is applied to the walls, conventional installation is used, except that the foil side is faced to the framing members or furring strips, whichever are being used. This will give the foil surface the air space that it needs for functioning properly.

FLEXIBLE INSULATION

Definition. Flexible insulations are loosely felted mats formed between tough paper or fabric. This is known as blanket or batt insulation. These insulations are flexible units 48 in. or more long. They are usually made to fit between the studs or ceiling joists and are made wide enough for either 16-in. or 24-in. spacings. The material is manufactured in controlled thicknesses and may be had either in folded sections packed in cartons or in rolls. It may be made of wood fiber, mineral wool, cotton, or animal hair. If the mats are not naturally fire resistant, they are made so by the company that manufactures them.

How to apply flexible insulation. Flexible insulation is usually applied in one of two ways: (1) between the framing members, held in place only by friction; (2) between the framing members, with nailing flanges nailed to the inside edges of the studs or other framing members. In the applying of all types of blanket insulation, no openings should be left through which air can move from one space to another. This precaution increases the efficiency of the insulation.

HOW TO PREVENT HEAT LOSS

Generally speaking, there are two ways in which heat is lost from a room or a house: (1) by the infiltration of cold air around windows, doors, cracks, etc.; (2) by direct transmission through the building materials.

It is possible for both types of heat losses to occur at the same window or door, part of it around the window at poorly fitted points and part of it directly through glass.

Methods of preventing infiltration of cold air:

1. By well-fitted doors
2. By well-fitted windows
3. By using shiplap siding and sheathing
4. By using good-grade building paper

5. By using good-grade metal weather strip
6. By using storm sash

Methods of preventing transmission of heat:

1. By thicker surface resistance
2. By using flexible insulation between wall studs
3. By using flexible insulation between ceiling joists
4. By using flexible insulation between rafters
5. By using rigid insulation board for sheathing

ATTIC INSULATION

One of the best kinds of attic insulation is the blanket type. It usually comes in rolls and is placed directly between the ceiling

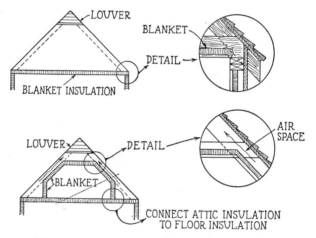

Figure 183. Proper installation of the blanket.

joists, rafters, or studs, as the case demands. In order to secure the greatest effectiveness of this installation, two things are most necessary:

1. Proper installation of the blanket (Figure 183).
2. Sufficient ventilation of the attic space between the insulation and the roof (Figure 184).

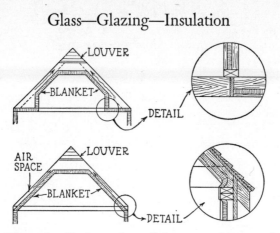

Figure 184. There should always be sufficient space between the insulation and the roof to permit the passage of air to the louver.

ADVANTAGES OF ATTIC INSULATION

1. Attic insulation effects appreciable fuel savings and increased comfort during the heating season.

2. With it the entire house can be made cooler and more comfortable during the summer months.

3. Insulation of the ceiling and roof construction is very effective because of the higher temperature at the ceiling line during the heating season, owing to the fact that warm air has a tendency to rise. In an uninsulated house, this temperature difference from floor to ceiling may be as high as 15 degrees. This causes a greater temperature difference between the air at the ceiling and outside, and a resulting higher heat loss through walls.

4. Attic insulation increases the temperature of the ceiling surface during the heating season more nearly to that of the room air temperature; therefore, drafts are reduced, and excessive loss of radiated heat from occupants to cold ceiling surface is reduced.

5. Uninsulated ceilings and roofs of ordinary construction offer in themselves little resistance to the passage of heat.

6. Many factors that contribute to excessive transfer of heat through roofs are not reckoned with in theoretical calculation, for instance, poor and open construction at the eaves.

7. The attic space is usually accessible for the easy installation of insulation.

HOW TO ESTIMATE INSULATION

Insulating boards, such as sheathing, wallboards, tile boards, plank-effect boards, pressed wood, hard board, plaster board, etc., are sold by the square foot. To find the number of square feet needed, simply determine the number of square feet in the room to be covered and in some cases allow a small percentage for cutting and waste. In some cases this is not necessary, if the boards are the right size to fit the spaces. Unless wall openings are unusually large, deductions are not made for them.

> *Example:* A room is 12 by 12 ft. square, with 8-ft. side walls.
> *Solution:* $12 \times 12 = 144$ sq. ft. in the ceiling
> $8 \times 12 \times 4 = 384$ sq. ft. in the side walls
> $384 + 144 = 528$ sq. ft. total
>
> If we were using insulating board 4 by 12 ft. long, each piece would contain 48 sq. ft.
>
> $$\frac{528}{48} = 11 \text{ pieces}$$
>
> At 10 cents per square foot, our cost would be
>
> $$\$0.10 \times 528 = \$52.80$$

Blanket insulation also is figured by the square foot. It is usually manufactured in rolls of 50 sq. ft. each. Thicknesses may vary from 1 in. to 4 in. This does not affect the area to be covered. However, the cost is always greater as the thickness increases. Costs are quoted by the square foot of a given thickness. To find the number of rolls needed, first determine the number of square feet in the area of the attic or side walls to be covered or insulated. Then divide this number by the number of square feet in the roll or carton.

Granulated insulations are usually sold by the bag. Most bags contain 40 lb. each. A 40-lb. bag will cover about 25 sq. ft. of area if spread 2 in. thick, 17 sq. ft. if spread 3 in. thick, 14 sq. ft. if spread 3½ in. thick, and 13 sq. ft. if spread 4 in. thick.

To find the number of bags needed, first determine the area to be covered in square feet. Then decide on the thickness to be used. If it is to be 4 in., then divide the total area in square feet by 13. This would give the number of bags needed.

Example: The attic space to be covered is 20 by 20 ft.
Solution: 20 × 20 = 400 sq ft.

Thickness to be used is 4 in.

$$\frac{400}{13} = 30.76 \text{ bags}$$

Since we cannot buy broken bags of material, we would need to order 31 bags. At $1.50 per bag, the insulation would cost:

$$31 \times \$1.50 = \$46.50$$

VENTILATION

Ventilation is considered one of the best methods of preventing condensation in buildings. Condensation may occur in the attic, in the walls, in the crawl space under the house, in basements, on windows, etc. Condensation is most likely to occur in houses at two specific times: (1) during the first 6 or 8 months after a house is built, and (2) in extreme cold weather when interior humidity is high.

Proper ventilation of the attic or under the roof allows moisture-laden attic air to escape during the winter heating season, and also allows the hot dry air of the summer season to do so.

Attic areas are usually ventilated by the use of louvers or ventilators. They may be:

1. Roof louvers (Figure 185)
2. Cornice ventilators (Figure 186)
3. Gable louvers (Figure 187)
4. Flat-roof ventilators (Figure 187)

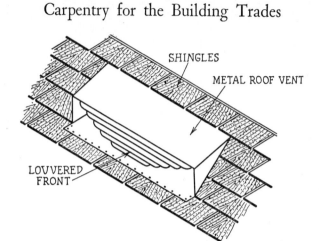

Figure 185. Roof louvers.

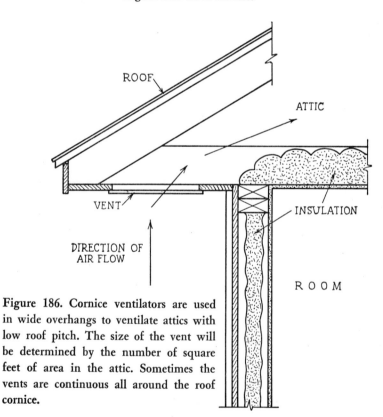

Figure 186. Cornice ventilators are used in wide overhangs to ventilate attics with low roof pitch. The size of the vent will be determined by the number of square feet of area in the attic. Sometimes the vents are continuous all around the roof cornice.

Attic ventilation. One of the most common methods of ventilating an attic is with the use of wood louver frames, some of which are used for the purpose of ventilating alone, while others are used for decorative purposes also. There are many types, sizes, and shapes of louvers. Following are the points to consider when building or designing a louver.

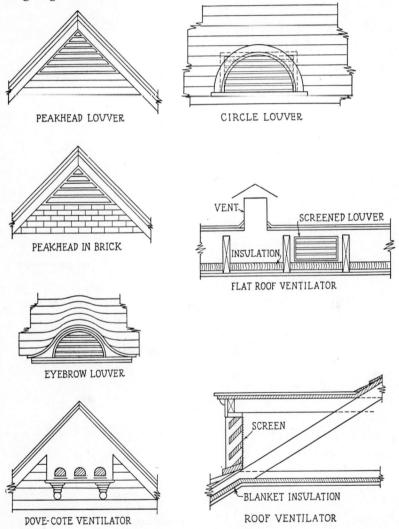

PEAKHEAD LOUVER

CIRCLE LOUVER

PEAKHEAD IN BRICK

VENT

SCREENED LOUVER

INSULATION

FLAT ROOF VENTILATOR

EYEBROW LOUVER

SCREEN

BLANKET INSULATION

ROOF VENTILATOR

DOVE-COTE VENTILATOR

Figure 187. Roof ventilators.

1. The minimum net open area should be ¼ sq. in. per sq. ft. of ceiling area in the attic.

2. Most louver frames are usually 5 in. wide.

3. Rabbet out the back edge for a screen or door, or both.

4. Use ¾-in. slats and space them about 1¾ in. apart.

5. Provide sufficient slant or slope to the slats to prevent rain from driving in.

6. For best operation, place the louver as near the top of a gable as possible.

Types of louvers. Some of the more commonly used louvers are the following (Figure 187):

1. Peakhead, in frame wall
2. Peakhead, in brick wall
3. Eyebrow louver
4. Dovecot louver
5. Half-circle louver

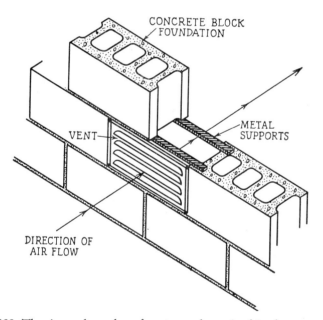

Figure 188. The size and number of vents are determined in the same manner as for attic ventilators.

6. Flat-roof louver

7. Flat dormer louver

Crawl-space ventilation. Crawl spaces under basementless houses should be well ventilated. This air circulation under the floors prevents excessive condensation, which would cause warping, swelling, twisting, and rotting of the lumber. These vents are usually called "foundation louvers" (Figure 188). They are set into the foundation as it is being built. A good foundation vent should be equipped with a copper or bronze screen and adjustable shutters for opening and closing the louver. The sizes for the louvers should be figured on the same basis as for attic louvers—$\frac{1}{4}$ in. for each square foot of under-floor space.

7

LUMBER—GRADING AND MEASURING

CLASSIFICATION

In general there are four classes of lumber:

1. Hardwood factory, for furniture, fixtures, etc.
2. Softwood factory, for doors, sash, cabinets, etc.
3. Yard lumber, for building and industrial work
4. Structural timbers, sizes over 6 in. wide and thick

Yard lumber is manufactured primarily for the building trades. It is worked into various forms, shapes, and sizes at the planing mills. This includes lumber for framework such as 2 by 4's, 2 by 6's, 2 by 8's, 2 by 10's, 2 by 12's, and all other framework sizes. It includes common boards, siding, sheathing, ceiling, partition lumber, flooring, moldings, casings, baseboards, shiplap, and all other general dimension stock. Yard lumber includes such woods as white pine, yellow pine, fir, spruce, redwood, and occasionally oak.

The classification shown in Table 23 is now being used for grading yard lumber.

TABLE 23. YARD LUMBER CLASSIFICATION

Total products of a typical log arranged in a series according to quality as determined by appearance.	1. *Select lumber* of a very good appearance and with very good finishing qualities.	Suitable for natural finishes	*Grade A.* Practically free from defects. *Grade B.* Allows a few small defects or blemishes.
		Suitable for paint finishes	*Grade C.* Allows a limited number of small defects or blemishes that can be covered with paint. *Grade D.* Allows any number of defects or blemishes that do not detract from a finished appearance when painted.
	2. *Common lumber* containing defects or blemishes which detract from a finished appearance but which is still suitable for general utility and construction purposes.	Suitable for use without waste	*No. 1 Common.* Sound and tight knotted stock. May be considered watertight stock. *No. 2 Common.* Allows large and coarse defects. May be considered graintight lumber.
		Lumber permitting waste	*No. 3 Common.* Allows larger and coarser defects than No. 2 and some knotholes. *No. 4 Common.* Low-quality lumber admitting the coarsest defects such as rot and holes.

DEFECTS AND BLEMISHES

A *defect* is considered to be any irregularity found in or on a piece that would lower its strength or durability. A *blemish* may be considered as any mars, scratches, or unsatisfactory appearance of the wood not classed as a defect. Defects and blemishes may be classed as follows:

1. Knots	8. Cross grain
2. Holes	9. Checks
3. Decay	10. Bad milling
4. Splits	11. Bark
5. Warp	12. Pith
6. Pitch pockets	13. Discoloration
7. Streaks	14. Gum pockets

A complete list of grading rules in detail may be secured from any lumber manufacturer's association. American lumber standards have been adopted by most of them.

LUMBER TERMS

In order to be able to measure lumber quickly and accurately, it is necessary to understand the following terms and their application to lumber:

Board foot. Lumber is measured by the board foot, which is a piece of lumber having an area of 1 sq. ft. on its flat surface and a thickness of 1 in. or less (Figure 189).

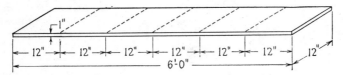

Figure 189. Board feet.

Feet. Feet is generally taken to mean board feet unless reference is made to linear feet.

Linear feet. Linear feet represent only the length of a board or piece, not any certain width.

Rough stock. Rough stock means lumber that is cut up into pieces larger than its intended use, or lumber that has not been dressed.

Dressed. By dressing lumber we mean planing or smoothing it. Lumber is cut and sawed in a sawmill. Since this process leaves the surface rough, it is necessary to dress the lumber, or plane it down to a smooth surface. This is done in a planing mill. It may be dressed on one face or both faces, or on both faces and both edges.

S. 1 S. Lumber dressed on one face is indicated by marking "S. 1 S.," which means surfaced on one side.

S. 2 S. Lumber dressed on two faces will be indicated by marking "S. 2 S.," meaning surfaced on two sides.

S. 4 S. Lumber dressed on both sides and both edges will be marked "S. 4 S."

Size. When lumber is dressed, it loses in size the amount planed off in shavings. A piece sawed at the mill 2 in. thick and 10 in. wide is called a "2 by 10." However, when it is dressed, it becomes $1\frac{3}{4}$ by $9\frac{5}{8}$ in., but it is still called a "2 by 10." In measuring the *width* of common rough lumber, a fraction of an inch equal to or greater than $\frac{1}{2}$ in. is counted as a whole inch, while a fraction less than $\frac{1}{2}$ in. is neglected. For example, a board $6\frac{1}{2}$ in. wide would be called 7 in. wide. A board $6\frac{5}{8}$ in. would be called 7 in. wide, and a board $6\frac{1}{4}$ in. would be called 6 in. wide.

Surfaced. A term generally applied to lumber that has been dressed only on the faces.

Jointed. Lumber that has been dressed on the edges is said to be "jointed."

Lumber. Pieces 5 in. or less in thickness.

Timber. The term applied to pieces more than 5 in. in thickness; also to standing trees. We may also speak of a piece as having in it "good timber."

Boards. Boards are pieces less than 2 in. thick and 8 in. or more wide.

Planks. Planks are yard lumber from 2 to 4 in. in thickness and 8 in. or over in width.

Strips. Strips are pieces less than 2 in. thick and not 8 in. wide.

Scantlings. Pieces from 2 to 5 in. thick and less than 8 in. wide.

Standard lengths. Most yard lumber is sold in standard lengths, as 10, 12, 14, 16, 18 ft., etc. When several boards of the same length but of different widths are to be measured, it is convenient to add all the widths together and figure the lot as one board.

TABLE 24. TO CALCULATE BOARD MEASURE

1 in. thick or less

Pieces 3" wide contain ¼ as many feet as they are long
Pieces 4" wide contain ⅓ as many feet as they are long
Pieces 6" wide contain ½ as many feet as they are long
Pieces 9" wide contain ¾ as many feet as they are long
Pieces 12" wide contain just as many feet as they are long
Pieces 15" wide contain 1¼ as many feet as they are long

HOW TO FIND THE NUMBER OF BOARD FEET

Multiply the number of square feet in the surface of a piece of lumber by the number of inches in its thickness, counting a thickness less than 1 in. the same as 1 in.

Example 1: Find the number of board feet in a piece of lumber 2 in. thick, 10 in. wide, and 6 ft. long.

Solution: $\dfrac{2 \times 10 \times 6}{12} = 10$, or 10 bd. ft.

The above method is known as the "cancellation" method. The whole process is expressed as a fraction. The numerator has three figures: the thickness in inches, the width in inches, and the length in *feet*. If these three dimensions are expressed in *inches,* then their product would have to be divided by 144 instead of 12, since there are 144 sq. in. in 1 sq. ft.

Example 2: Find the number of board feet in a piece of lumber 2 in. thick, 10 in. wide, and 102 in. long.

Solution: $\dfrac{2 \times 10 \times 102}{144} = 14\frac{1}{6}$, or $14\frac{1}{6}$ bd. ft.

Example 3: Find the total number of board feet in the following pieces: 21 pieces, 1 in. thick, 4 in. wide, and 9 ft. long.

Solution: $\dfrac{21 \times 1 \times 4 \times 9}{12} = 63$, or 63 bd. ft.

PLYWOOD

In most house construction where panel plywood is used, Douglas fir is considered one of the best. Douglas-fir plywood is a built-up board of laminated veneers in which the grain of each piece is at right angles to the one adjacent to it. Kiln-dried veneer is united under high pressure with a bonding agent, which makes the joints as strong as the wood itself or stronger. The alternating direction of the grain with each contiguous layer of wood equalizes the strains and in this way minimizes shrinkage and warpage. It also prevents splitting.

Plywood panels, size 48 in. wide and 96 in. long, are very popular in the building of houses. However, they are made in many other sizes, from 30 in. wide to 144 in. long, and in various thicknesses. Thicknesses are from ¼ in. to ¾ in. Other sizes are specially made. The stock panel width of 48 in., as well as the popular 8-ft. lengths, are multiples of 16 in., which is the accepted spacing for studs and joists.

In building construction, plywoods have many uses. They are extensively used in the following types of construction:

1. Kitchen cabinets, bookcases, shelves, linen closets, utility-room cabinets, supply cases, and many other types of cabinet work
2. Interior wall paneling, partition walls, and for decorative purposes
3. Exterior wall sheathing

4. Exterior roof sheathing
5. Subflooring and underlays
6. Outside wall siding
7. Concrete form work
8. Outside decorations, soffits, etc.

Plywoods are also obtainable in many species of wood other than fir. They may be with veneers of oak, birch, walnut, maple, mahogany, white pine, yellow pine, and almost any other woods desired. These panels are, however, used mostly for cabinetwork and inside-finish work. Plywoods may be worked in the same manner as any other wood. The most satisfactory power-saw cutting is done with a hollow-ground combination saw, files with little hook. For regular handsawing, a regular crosscut is very satisfactory. Ripsaws are not generally used for cutting plywood panels, regardless of the grain direction.

Plywood has excellent nail-bearing and holding properties, even when the nails are close to the edge of the board. The thickness of the panels and the type of work being done will determine the size of nails to be used. Plywood panels are sold by the square foot. Any panel 1 in. or less in thickness and 12 in. by 12 in. is considered a board foot.

RED-CEDAR CLOSET LINING

Red-cedar closet lining is cedarwood material used to line clothes and storage closets. Made in much the same manner as oak flooring, it is tongued and grooved and end-matched. It is usually put up in bundles or cartons containing 40 ft., board measure, each. Cedar lining is usually manufactured $\frac{3}{8}$ in. thick, $3\frac{1}{4}$ in. wide, and in random lengths. A 40-foot bundle or carton will cover about 30 sq. ft. of actual space. To figure the amount of cedar lining needed, determine the number of actual square feet to be covered, and then add to this number 25 per cent.

KNOTTY-PINE PANELING

Knotty-pine side-wall finishes have become very popular, especially in ranch-style houses. In present-day residence design, the trend is toward simplicity and knotty-pine wall treatment helps to produce this effect. While it may be used in any room, it is very adaptable to game rooms, recreation areas, dens, study rooms, boys' rooms, utility rooms, etc. It is not uncommon to have the side walls of a room treated with knotty-pine paneling and the ceilings plastered.

Knotty-pine matched-edge panel boards may be secured, along with other millwork, from the dealer's regular source of supply.

Knotty-pine paneling may be installed over new framing or it may be installed over old, plastered walls. It is usually applied vertically and nailed to strips which have been installed horizontally around the room. A wide mold is used at the top at the ceiling line, and regular baseboard and trim are used elsewhere, the same as in the rest of the house. Sometimes the baseboards are omitted.

Knotty-pine panel boards usually have one side V-jointed and beaded, while the other side is V-jointed only. Either side can be left exposed, depending upon the effect desired.

Most knotty-pine material comes $\frac{3}{4}$ in. thick and $5\frac{1}{2}$, $7\frac{1}{2}$, $9\frac{1}{2}$, or $11\frac{1}{2}$ in. wide. All joints are usually shiplapped and the boards are counted as 1 by 6, 1 by 8, 1 by 10, 1 by 12, etc. The lengths will run from 6 to 16 ft. long.

To find the amounts of knotty-pine panel boards needed for a room, first determine the actual number of square feet to be covered and add to that 15 per cent more for the total number of board feet to be ordered.

8

SCAFFOLDS AND SAFETY MEASURES

SCAFFOLDS

In practically all stages of construction, scaffolds of various types are needed. Each kind of work requires its own type of scaffold. A strong, well-built, and safe platform built at the right height enables a man to do more work and do it better and more efficiently in less time. However, on the small construction job, building a good scaffold usually takes more time than does the actual job itself. The material used for scaffolding should be clean, clear, and free from knots and imperfections. It should be straight-grained and not easily broken.

Types of scaffolds. Scaffolds may be either of the following types: (1) swinging or (2) fixed. Scaffolds may either be swung from some point above the working level, or be built up to the working level from a firm and substantial base or foundation. For the security of the workman employed, all types should comply with the safety laws. Care should be taken to see that the structure is built to protect not only the men working on it but also those working under it.

Guard rails built about 3½ or 4 ft. high at the back of the platform should be provided to prevent the men from falling off. Foot boards should be laid close enough together to prevent tools and materials from falling through.

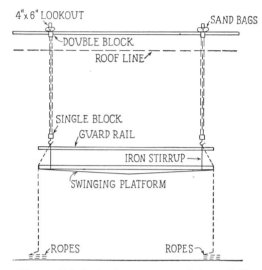

Figure 190. Swinging, or suspended, scaffold.

Swinging scaffolds. *Swinging* or suspended scaffolds are generally used by painters (Figure 190). They are used on high flat-top buildings or those too high to reach from an extension ladder. Such a scaffold consists of a platform supported by blocks and falls which are fastened to 4- by 6-in. lookouts that extend out over the edge of the wall (Figure 191). The inside ends of these lookouts are generally weighted down with sandbags or other suitable weights.

Sometimes a building with a wide cornice will require a special U hanger in order to prevent injury to the cornice (Figure 192). Such a device will hang in close to the wall.

The *gable* or *sloped-back roof* is generally difficult to provide with a swinging scaffold. This can be done, however, with a double block and cable, as shown in Figure 193.

How to build a swinging scaffold and rigging. To build a swinging scaffold you will need two iron stirrups (Figure 194) made of

¾- or 1-in. iron rod. A smaller iron can be welded to the stirrup near the top for the guard rail. The platform should be about 2 ft. wide and 18 ft. long (Figure 195). Tapered 2- by 6-in. pieces with a No. 9 wire stretched around them will make the truss (Figure 196).

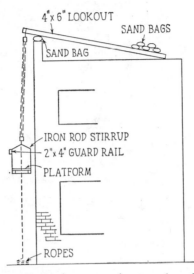

Figure 191. Lookout extends over edge of wall.

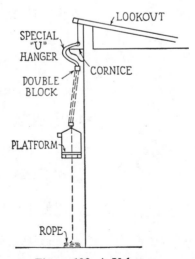

Figure 192. A U hanger.

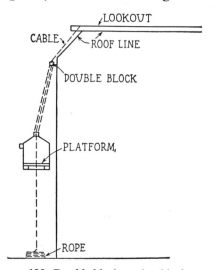

Figure 193. Double-block and cable hanger.

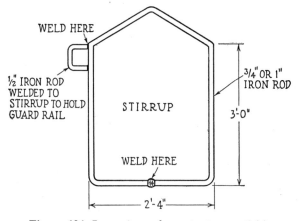

Figure 194. Iron stirrup for swinging scaffold.

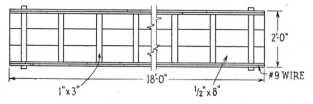

Figure 195. Swinging platform, or stage.

Use a 2 by 4 for the guard rail. Also two double blocks, two single blocks, and two ¾-in. ropes of the desired length will be needed.

Test the scaffold before using it. Raise it a short distance from the ground and have two or three men, or something of equal

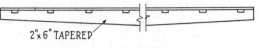

2"x 6" TAPERED

Figure 196. Tapered truss.

weight, try it out. Frequent inspections should be made of all scaffolding and rigging to prevent accidents.

Figure 197 shows a method of scaffolding a barn roof of the Gothic type. Use a 2 by 8, or a 2 by 10 for the walk board, and

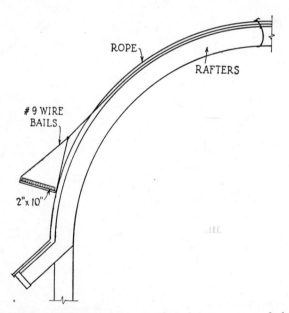

ROPE

RAFTERS

#9 WIRE
BAILS

2"x 10"

Figure 197. Raise scaffold from above. After the steep part of the roof has been passed, ordinary roof brackets may be used.

suspend it from above with ropes about 14 ft. long. Pass No. 9 wire through holes near the edges of the planks so that they will stay in place. Strap iron can be employed here instead of wire.

Fixed scaffolds. There are many types of fixed scaffolds. Following are some of the more commonly used: (1) pole scaffolds, (2) horse scaffolds, (3) outrigger scaffolds, (4) rolling platform scaf-

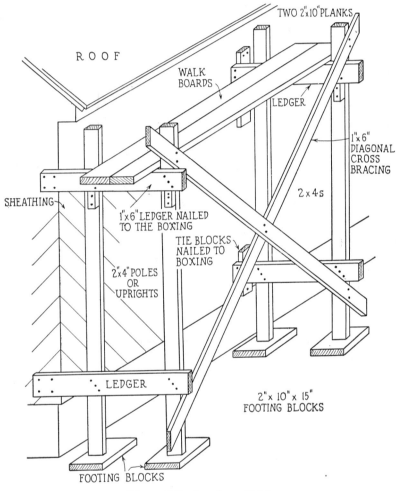

Figure 198. A pole scaffold.

folds, (5) wood and metal jacks, (6) roof brackets, (7) ladder jacks, (8) putlogs, (9) roof jacks, (10) squares.

Pole scaffolds are rapidly being replaced by various types of smaller iron scaffolding which can be put up and taken down very quickly. However, it is still necessary at times and in some places to use pole scaffolds (Figure 198). These are so called because they are built up from 2 by 4's or 2 by 6's set on end on a firm base. They

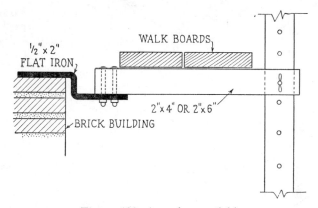

Figure 199. A putlog scaffold.

should be well tied together with ledgers to hold the foot boards and should also be well braced diagonally. All pole scaffolding should be tied well to the building and nailed securely. For brick buildings putlogs are used (Figure 199).

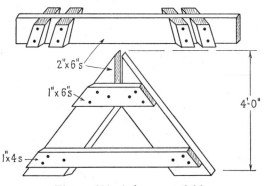

Figure 200. A horse scaffold.

Horse scaffolds are used extensively in building construction as they are light, portable, and easy to make. Generally they are made demountable (Figure 200). Horse scaffolds are made about 4 ft.

high; by placing one tier on top of another, increased height may be obtained. However, these scaffolds are not suitable for heavy loads.

Outrigger scaffolds are platforms supported by beams or framework fastened to the floor or other parts of the frame of a building. This type of scaffold is used where repairs are to be made at some

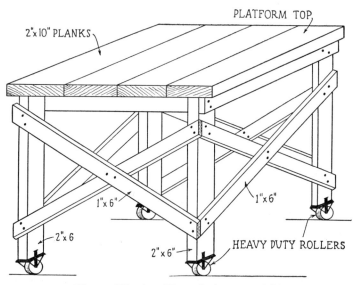

Figure 201. A rolling platform scaffold.

point above ground level so high that building up from the ground would not be economical, as in repairing church steeples and towers.

Rolling platform scaffolds are used on inside work, usually where floors will permit (Figure 201). The entire frame is constructed of 2 by 6's with 1- by 6-in. braces and 2- by 10-in. floor boards. A built-on ladder permits easy access.

Wood and metal jacks are favorites with most carpenters because they are portable and easy to move from place to place (Figure 202). Metal wall brackets are used to nail on siding, or sheathing, set window frames, and for many other types of work. The upper ends are nailed securely to the studs. The lower ends are nailed to a

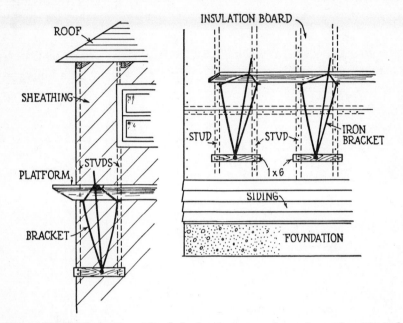

Figure 202. Nail the top ends of the brackets securely to the studs with 16*d* common nails. Under the bottom end place a piece of 1 by 6 and nail it to the studs with 8*d* common nails.

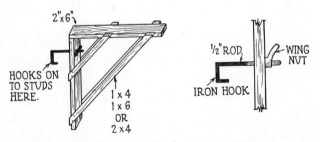

Figure 203. How to make wooden-scaffold jacks.

1 by 6, which in turn is nailed to the studs. Wood jacks may also be made, as shown in Figure 203.

Roof brackets are used mostly while laying shingles or roofing. There are many types made of iron and wood (Figure 204). These brackets can usually be bought cheaper than one can make them.

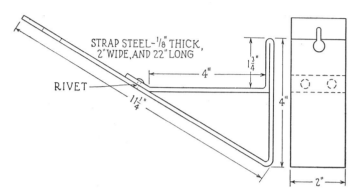

Figure 204. Roof brackets.

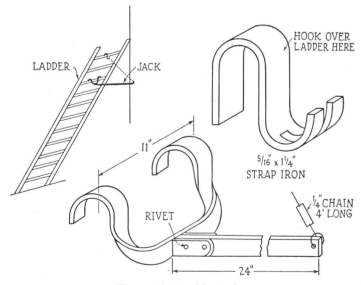

Figure 205. Ladder jacks.

Ladder jacks are metal braces applied to the rounds of a ladder (Figure 205). Two ladders are used, each with a jack on it, and these jacks carry a 2 by 10 for a walk board. This type of scaffold is not recommended for high construction work.

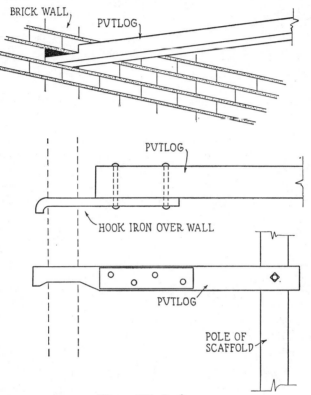

Figure 206. Putlogs.

Putlogs are used on buildings constructed of brick or masonry, usually brick veneer buildings (Figure 206). They are used with pole backs and can be adjustable or just nailed in place on the pole. When the work is completed, the putlog is removed by pulling it out and filling or pointing up the hole left by it.

Roof jacks (Figure 207) are a type of roof scaffold that is easy to build, portable, and adjustable; also easy to take down and put up. If roof ladders are not available, use ordinary ladders. Either wire

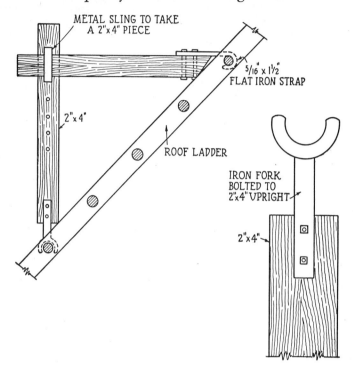

Figure 207. If regular roof ladders are not available, use ordinary ladders and anchor the top end to the other side of the building.

one ladder to another at the top and hang it on the other side of the roof, or tie ropes to the tops of the ladders and anchor the ropes down on the other side of the building.

Squares are used mostly by brick masons and are made 4 ft. 6 in. square. They are made from 2 by 4's and 1 by 6's (Figure 208). As soon as the brick mason is above his foot scaffold, the squares are set up along the wall or work. Braces made of 1 by 6's or 1 by 8's should be nailed on diagonally. The entire top is then planked with a 2 by 10 for a working platform. When the second set of squares is set up for more height, all the 2 by 10 planks are removed except the two outside ones, which are left to hold up the second tier of squares and to help brace the entire scaffold.

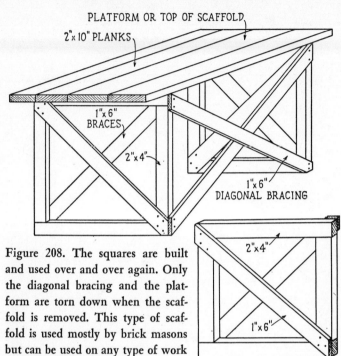

PLATFORM OR TOP OF SCAFFOLD
2"x 10" PLANKS
1"x 6" BRACES
2"x 4"
1"x 6" DIAGONAL BRACING
2"x 4"
1"x 6"

Figure 208. The squares are built and used over and over again. Only the diagonal bracing and the platform are torn down when the scaffold is removed. This type of scaffold is used mostly by brick masons but can be used on any type of work where platforms are needed.

How to make a safe chimney scaffold. When a chimney top is being constructed or repaired, a scaffold is needed that will not damage or injure the roof (Figure 209). As the carpenter is called upon to do all such work, a great deal of time can be saved by using a scaffold as shown here.

1. Cut two 2 by 4's, each 3 ft. long.

2. Hinge these together at the top with an 8- or 10-in. taper hinge.

3. Cut two uprights of 2 by 4, 24 in. long.

4. Nail the 2 by 4's together at the corner and brace with 1 by 4's.

5. On the under side nail two 1- by 4-in. braces about 5 ft. long. The scaffold legs will rest on this and thus form a protection for the roof.

6. Build two sets of these and cover with 2 by 8's or 2 by 10's for walk boards.

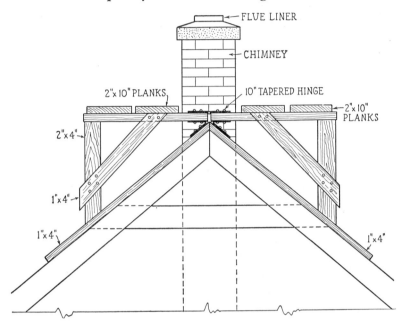

Figure 209. How to build a safe and portable chimney scaffold. This type of scaffold does not damage the roof and is very easy to move and to dismantle.

SAFETY MEASURES IN THE BUILDING TRADES

"Seldom is a *good* mechanic injured."

The first and most important factor in safety measures is the attitude of the worker himself toward safety. This is most necessary in reducing accidents in any work situation. The second factor is in knowing the correct and the safe way to handle or use all equipment. The best attitude comes only from a worker who has a deep interest in his job. A good attitude and a deep interest in his work are not sufficient, however, unless tools, machinery, and equipment are also kept in first-class mechanical condition. For example, a dull circular-saw blade would be extremely dangerous to use, regardless of how much interest a man had in his work, how much knowledge of safety he had, or how good his attitude was.

Hand tools should be kept in good condition at all times. Keep handles tight and never use broken tools for anything. Keep your stock and materials in order and floors clean at all times. This is most essential in the building trades. The most troublesome factor in causing accidents in the building trades is the inclination of work-men to be careless, not to keep their minds on their work, and to gamble with their lives just to save a few minutes of time. This is particularly true in building and using scaffolds.

The following are a few good rules for safety that the builder should always observe:

Safety rules for power machinery

1. Never operate a power saw, sander, or any machine unless you have been instructed in its operation.

2. Never operate any machine without the safety guards in place.

3. Be sure that your machine is grounded. Stand on a wooden platform whenever possible while operating power machinery.

4. Use an extension of sufficient size and length to do your job with easy operation.

5. Do not walk or step on drop cords or extension cords.

6. Never use electric current on a job unless the circuit is properly fused and grounded.

7. Do not start your cut on a saw, whether portable or stationary, until the saw has picked up full speed.

8. Remove all nails from stock before cutting it on a power saw.

9. Lumber with cement, plaster, lime, etc., adhering to it should never be run through power machines.

10. While sawing off blocks, boards, and ends, watch below, that falling pieces do not hit another workman.

Personal safety rules

1. Always wear a pair of overalls or clothes specially designed for the work you are doing.

2. It is better not to wear rings or other jewelry, loose-fitting clothing, or long neckties. They are likely to become caught in ma-chinery, on nails, or on scaffolding.

3. Always conduct yourself in the best workmanlike manner. You are always judged by your actions.

4. Loud and unnecessary talking should be avoided.

5. Never attempt to work if you do not feel well. Climbing on roofs, scaffolds, etc., in this condition may cause dizziness.

6. Never attempt a job where scaffolds are needed unless a safe and sturdy one has been built.

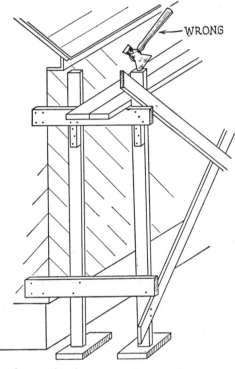

Figure 210. Never leave a hatchet, ax, or sharp tool of any kind stuck into a scaffold or any place where it might fall on a fellow workman.

7. Never carry sharp tools in your pockets. This includes open blades, chisels, dividers, etc.

8. Keep materials picked up from the floor or in places where you are working or where you have to walk or pass.

9. Do not work with a pencil in your mouth. Do not carry nails in your mouth.

10. Always put oily rags and waste in an iron container, or take

them out and burn them. This will prevent spontaneous combustion and possible fires.

11. Keep your hands as clean as you can for the work you are doing.

12. Do not try to work on substitute scaffolds. Inverted boxes, barrels, nail kegs, etc., make poor platforms, ladders, or scaffolds.

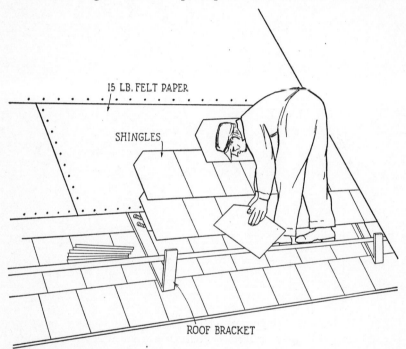

15 LB. FELT PAPER

SHINGLES

ROOF BRACKET

Figure 211. Always keep your eyes open. Do not walk off the end of a scaffold or step off the edge of a roof.

General safety practice

1. Always place a ladder on good sound footing. This prevents tipping or sliding to one side.

2. Do not attempt to reach heights beyond the length of your ladder. *Get a longer one.*

3. When using ladder jacks, see that they are fastened securely in place.

4. Never use a ladder with a broken round in it. You will forget that it is missing and will fall.

5. Keep your hammer handles tight. A loose one will let the head fly off and hurt a fellow workman.

6. Always hold a nail until it is well started into the wood. A glancing blow might cause it to fly into someone's eye.

Figure 212. Do not attempt work of this type without sufficient protection. Use ladders, guards, roof brackets, or scaffolds where it is at all possible.

7. Do not attempt to work on a roof or a scaffold when it is wet or has frost on it. You may slip and fall to the ground.

8. Never let tools or material slip or slide from a roof or scaffold. It will invariably fall on someone.

9. Never lay a hammer down. Always carry it in your hammer strap in your overalls.

10. Hatchets and axes should not be left where they will fall. They should never be stuck into the end of a scaffold or other places (Figure 210). Put them back into your toolbox after you have used them.

11. Do not attempt to carry or lift more than you can handle.

12. Always keep your eyes open and do not walk into an unguarded stair well, open hole, flue well, off the end of a scaffold, off the edge of the roof, or from any of the many places found during the construction of a house with little or no guarding. It is impossible to guard all of these at all times (Figures 211, 212).

9

BLUEPRINTS AND SPECI-
FICATIONS

BLUEPRINTS

How to read blueprints. It is essential that students of building trades be able to do simple blueprint reading, that is, know how to interpret working drawings, or blueprints. To read a blueprint, one must be able to picture or visualize in his mind the object as it will appear after it is made or built. He must be able to get from the blueprints such information as shapes, sizes, methods of construction, locations of various parts, kinds of materials used, etc. He should be able to interpret all the symbols and notations concerning the job.

The building trades student should first remember that a blueprint is a *record of instructions* given to him. Second, he should realize that the language used by the draftsman in making his drawings is largely a language of lines and that, unless the student can read and understand these lines, the instructions on a blueprint are merely a foreign language.

When a set of house plans are to be read, one should first study the several views until he has a mental picture of what is to be constructed. As a blueprint is a flat surface, it is necessary for the workman to use his imagination to make the lines and views lift up from the paper into their natural and intended planes.

Views. A drawing or plan usually represents a view of some one thing. Consider, for example, the house in Figure 213. In your imagination see the view from several sides. If you stand directly out in front of the house and look directly at it, you will get the front

Figure 213. If you stand directly in front of the house and look directly at the front of it, you will see a "front view."

view. You will note that this view appears as a flat wall. You do not see any of the sides or the back of the house. This front view in house plans is usually called the *front elevation* (Figure 214). It shows the height of the house, the style of windows, the kind of siding material, and the general shape.

If you stand out at the right side of the house and look directly at the end of it, you see an *end view* or *right side elevation*. If you stand on the left side and look directly at the end of it, you see another end view, the *left side elevation*. If you stand in the rear of the house and look directly at it, you see a *rear view,* or *rear elevation*.

Thus you have established: (1) the front elevation, (2) the right side elevation, (3) the left side elevation, (4) the rear elevation (Figure 214). Sometimes these are expressed in terms of north, east, west, and south elevations. These, of course, are established only after a definite location for the house has been determined.

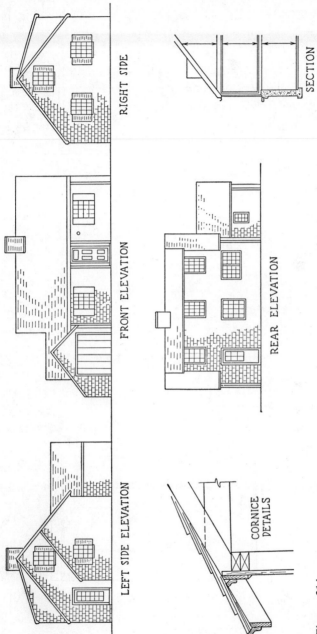

RIGHT SIDE

SECTION

FRONT ELEVATION

REAR ELEVATION

LEFT SIDE ELEVATION

CORNICE
DETAILS

Figure 214.

257

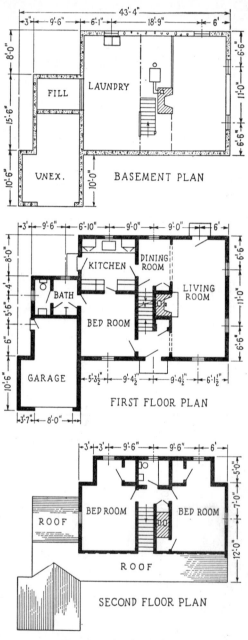

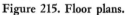

Figure 215. Floor plans.

House plans. Ordinary house plans may be grouped as follows:

Plans:	Elevations:	Details:
Plot plan	Front elevation	Construction details
Basement plan	Right side elevation	Cabinet details
First-floor plan	Left side elevation	Finish details
Second-floor plan	Rear elevation	Architectural details
Roof plan	Sectional elevation	Material details

Plans. Plans are views taken in the horizontal plane. For example, take a large sheet of glass and hold it directly over the top of the house. By so doing you establish a horizontal plane. If you look through this glass and draw upon its surface an outline of the top of the house and roof, you have drawn a top view or an outline of the *roof plan* in the *horizontal plane*.

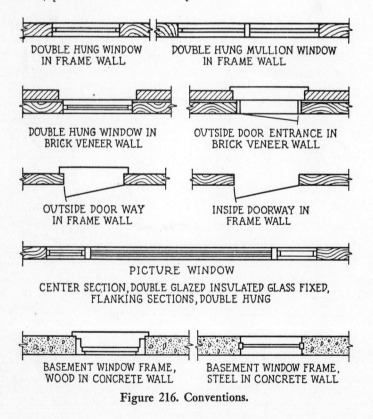

DOUBLE HUNG WINDOW
IN FRAME WALL

DOUBLE HUNG MULLION WINDOW
IN FRAME WALL

DOUBLE HUNG WINDOW IN
BRICK VENEER WALL

OUTSIDE DOOR ENTRANCE IN
BRICK VENEER WALL

OUTSIDE DOOR WAY
IN FRAME WALL

INSIDE DOORWAY IN
FRAME WALL

PICTURE WINDOW

CENTER SECTION, DOUBLE GLAZED INSULATED GLASS FIXED,
FLANKING SECTIONS, DOUBLE HUNG

BASEMENT WINDOW FRAME,
WOOD IN CONCRETE WALL

BASEMENT WINDOW FRAME,
STEEL IN CONCRETE WALL

Figure 216. Conventions.

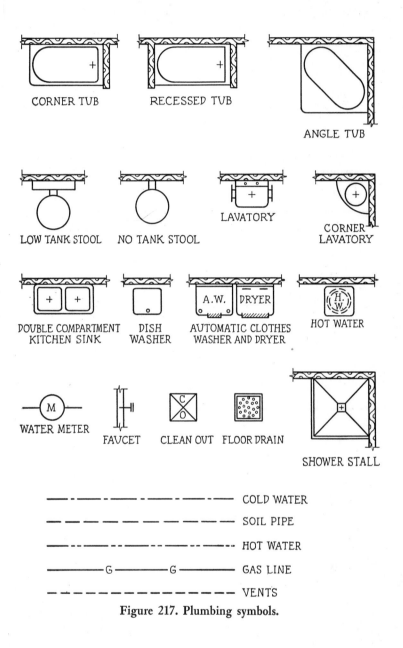

Figure 217. Plumbing symbols.

Floor plans are drawn in the same manner, except that they represent only a cross section of the house and are taken at about 3 ft. above each floor level. They are really top views of these cross sections (Figure 215).

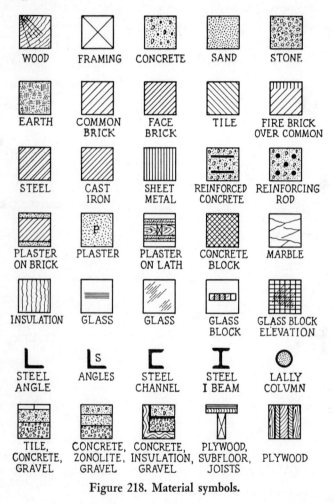

Figure 218. Material symbols.

Elevations. Elevations are views taken in the vertical plane. For example, stand again directly in front of the house and hold a large sheet of glass in a vertical position. In doing this you establish a vertical plane. If you look through the glass and draw upon its surface an outline of the front of the house, you have drawn an outline of the *front elevation* in the *vertical plane*.

Details. Details are drawings usually at a larger scale than the rest of the house, showing such things as construction, finish, and

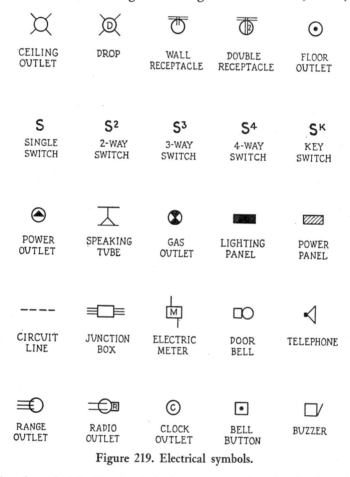

| CEILING OUTLET | DROP | WALL RECEPTACLE | DOUBLE RECEPTACLE | FLOOR OUTLET |

| S | S^2 | S^3 | S^4 | S^K |
| SINGLE SWITCH | 2-WAY SWITCH | 3-WAY SWITCH | 4-WAY SWITCH | KEY SWITCH |

| POWER OUTLET | SPEAKING TUBE | GAS OUTLET | LIGHTING PANEL | POWER PANEL |

| CIRCUIT LINE | JUNCTION BOX | ELECTRIC METER | DOOR BELL | TELEPHONE |

| RANGE OUTLET | RADIO OUTLET | CLOCK OUTLET | BELL BUTTON | BUZZER |

Figure 219. Electrical symbols.

kinds of material. Figure 214 shows a cornice detail, because it would be difficult to show this feature in elevations.

Symbols. Symbols are representations that have been more or less standardized to represent various items and methods of construction in their field. House plans, of course, would include symbols from all the divisions of the building trades, such as carpentry,

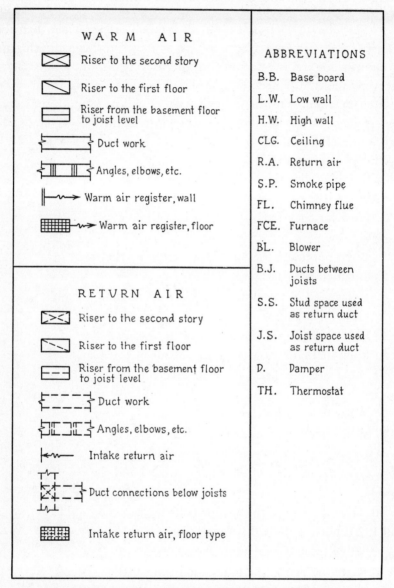

Figure 220. Symbols and abbreviations for heating plans.

plumbing, wiring, masonry, and many others. In order to interpret a drawing, one should be able to recognize the symbols found thereon. Some of the more common symbols are shown in Figures 216, 217, 218, 219, and 220.

Dimensions are lines, arrows, and figures used to indicate various sizes, positions, distances, etc., on the plans.

Interpretation. On the following pages will be found a complete set of plans and specifications for a ranch-style, three-bedroom, modern house (Figures 216 to 226).

Plot plan (Figure 221)

1. In which direction does the house face?
2. What is the size of the lot?
3. How far back from the street is the house set?
4. How wide is the driveway?
5. What public utilities are shown entering the lot?

Foundation plan (Figure 222)

1. What kind of material is used in the foundation walls?
2. How thick is the foundation of the house proper?
3. How thick is the foundation of the garage?
4. How many bearing posts are shown in this plan?
5. What are the sizes of the poured-concrete bearing-post footings?
6. What type girders are used?
7. What size floor joists are used?
8. How far apart are the floor joists spaced?
9. Give the number of floor joists needed and the lengths of each group.
10. Give the size of the anchor bolts used in the foundation.
11. To what scale is this foundation plan drawn?
12. How many foundation vents are shown?
13. Give the size of the foundation vents used.

Floor plan (Figure 223)

1. How many rooms are shown in the floor plan?
2. Name each room and give its size.

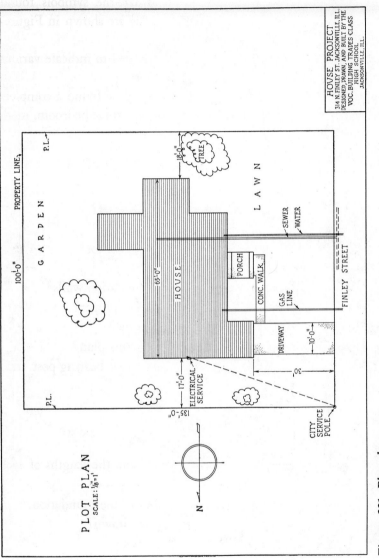

Figure 221. Plot plan.

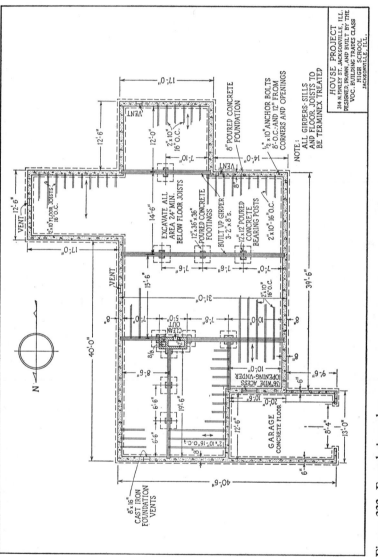

Figure 222. Foundation plan.

266

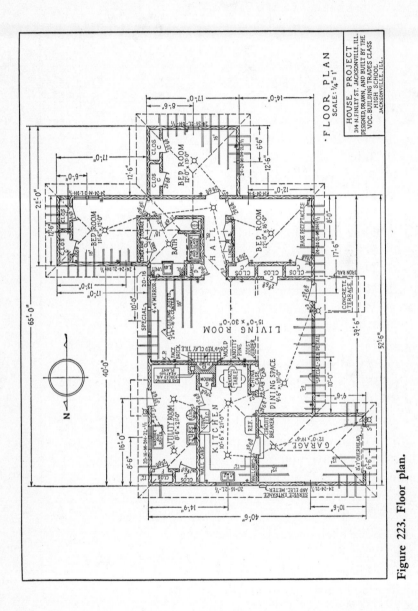

Figure 223. Floor plan.

267

3. What kind of walls is indicated?

4. How many single windows are shown?

5. How many double windows are shown?

6. How many triple windows are shown?

7. How many picture windows are shown?

8. Name the plumbing fixtures shown in the bathroom.

9. How many linen-storage cabinets are shown?

10. How many clothes closets are shown?

11. What type of heating system is used?

12. How many interior doors are needed? Give their sizes.

13. How many exterior doors are needed? Give their sizes.

14. How many electric ceiling outlets are shown?

15. How many electric wall outlets are shown?

16. How many base receptacles are shown in the plan?

17. How many three-way switches are called for?

18. What size ceiling joists are used?

19. What type garage door is used?

20. What materials are used for the hearth and the fireplace mantel?

Front and south elevations (Figure 224)

1. What is the total distance across the front of the house?

2. What kind of siding is used on the house?

3. How wide and how thick are the wall footings?

4. What is the minimum crawl-space height?

5. How many shutters and what sizes are needed in the front elevation?

6. What type, size, and gage gutters and downfalls are shown?

7. How wide an overhang is shown at the soffit?

8. What pitch does the roof have?

9. What size, kind, and weight of shingles are used?

10. Where are splash blocks used? Give their sizes.

Rear and north elevations (Figure 225)

1. How high are the ceilings?

2. What is the size of the rear terrace?

3. How many sash are used in each picture window?

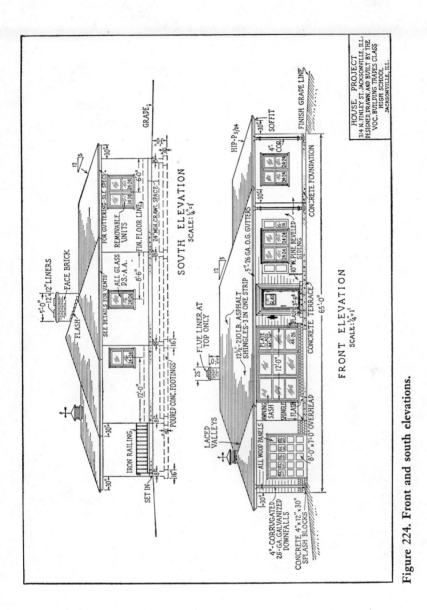

Figure 224. Front and south elevations.

269

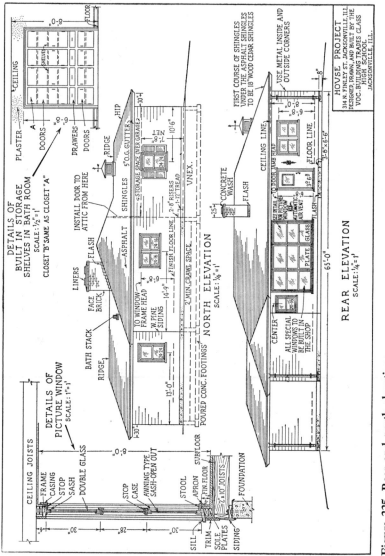

Figure 225. Rear and north elevations.

270

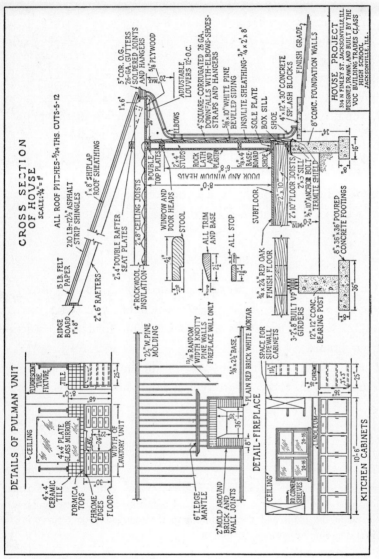

Figure 226. Section of house and details.

271

4. How many of the picture-window sash are awning type?
5. How many of the picture-window sash are fixed?
6. How high are the window and door heads set?

Cross section and details (Figure 226)

1. What size rafter material is used?
2. What type wall sheathing is used?
3. What type roof sheathing is used?
4. What type framing is used in the construction of this house?
5. What kind of insulation is called for in the attic?
6. Indicate the size and kind of finish floor used.
7. What is the size of the plate glass mirror used in the bathroom?
8. Give the height of the base section of the kitchen cabinets.
9. What kind of material is used to make the soffit?

SPECIFICATIONS

Almost all house plans are accompanied by a set of specifications. These are *statements* of *particulars* which tell you what you are going to receive in materials and workmanship for the construction of your house.

The following specifications are for the house described in the accompanying figures and are typical frame-house specifications.

SPECIFICATIONS

For the construction of a ranch-style house for

NAME: _____

Precedence. Detailed instruction shall govern over-all general instructions, and detailed drawings shall govern over-all general drawings. Should there be any conflict between the plans and the specifications, the same shall be referred to the architect for adjustments.

Drawings and specifications. The drawings shall be considered a part of and illustrative of these specifications. They shall be referred to and considered cooperative, and it shall not be the province of these specifications to mention any portion of the construction which the drawings are competent to explain. The decision of the architect as to the proper interpretation of his drawings shall be final. Before ordering any materials or doing any work, the contractor shall verify all measurements and check the same and shall thereafter be responsible for the same.

Bond. The contractor shall furnish either a personal bond or a surety bond acceptable to the owners, which will guarantee the full performance of the contract, and the payment of all obligations incurred by the contractor in the performance of the same. The contractor shall before final payment present waivers of lien for all materials used in the construction of this job. The same shall be done for all labor.

These shall save the owner harmless of responsibility for suit to collect money due for labor or material used in the construction of this house.

Protection. The contractor shall be responsible for his own and his employees' and his subcontractors' carelessness and mishaps and shall therefore protect himself at all times against this or its cause.

Water, electricity, power, and gas. The contractor shall make provision for all water, electricity, power, gas, etc., used on the job and in the performance of this work and shall pay for the same unless otherwise specified and decided upon between him and the owners.

Time and completion of work. Work under these plans and specifications shall be completed at a date mutually satisfactory to the contractor and to the owners. Such a date shall be written into the contract.

Payments. A written agreement as to payments and the amounts and when they are to be made should be drawn up before the work is started, or mutually agreed upon between the owners and the contractors.

Laws and permits. The contractor hereby binds himself to protect the owners and save them harmless during the execution of this work and thereafter from all damages arising from accidents, or from violations of public laws or ordinances of the city or from obstructions of any kind encountered during the erection of this work.

Materials and workmanship. Unless otherwise noted, all materials shall be new and of the best grade possible. All workmanship shall be first class. Substitutes shall be used only by the approval of the owners and the architect.

Extras. Bills for extras shall be allowed only when work or material or both has been ordered in writing after an agreement has been reached between the owners, architect, and the contractor.

Insurance. During this construction and until the final payment has been made, the contractor shall protect his equity and that of his material dealers against fire and other destructive forces. The owners in turn shall be responsible for the protection of their equity in the building as signified by the payments made on the contract, and will cover themselves to that extent by the means of insurance. The contractor shall protect his employees and his subcontractors with Workmen's Compensation Insurance.

Guarantee. The contractor shall guarantee his work and that of his subcontractors, for a period of one year from the date of the final payment, on the work, against any and all defects in workmanship or materials.

1. Excavation. All excavations for all walls and footings, pier posts, etc., shall be made as shown on the plans. The foundation shall be laid out square and true according to the sizes shown on the plans.

The grade level for the top of the foundation shall be furnished by the architect before the work is started. All excavations for the walls and footings shall be at least 18 in. below the present grade lines and at least 36 in. below the finished grade lines. The top of the foundation shall show only 8 in. above the finished grade line.

Grading shall be dropped around the garage as shown. All grading shall be complete as shown on the elevations and shall include the finished grading.

There shall be left a minimum crawl space under the house over the entire area of 2 ft. in the clear from the underside of the floor joists to the ground.

The entire area of ground surface under the house shall be treated with a spray coat of Terminix oil or equal, 1 gal. to each 100 sq. ft. of ground surface.

2. Concrete work. All foundation walls, bearing posts, and footings shall be of poured concrete. All concrete used on the job shall be of Ready Mix from an approved plant. All forms for all concrete work where needed shall be built square and true and shall be of such rigidity as to hold the concrete in place without bulging.

There shall be built a front and back terrace as shown. There shall also be built of concrete a front walk, steps, garage floor, garage-door apron, and splash blocks for the drains. The concrete walk shall extend from the front terrace to the driveway as shown. The walk shall be 4 in. thick, 4 ft. wide, and shall be marked off in 4-ft. sections. The concrete apron in front of the garage shall be 4 in. thick, 2 ft. wide, and 10 ft. long.

The garage floor shall be of poured concrete, 4 in. thick, troweled smooth and made with a drain of ⅛ in. to the foot to the front doors.

All concrete work shall be troweled smooth on the finish surfaces.

There shall be installed copper or aluminum flashings at all intersections of concrete construction with the house or woodwork. The subhearth for the fireplace shall be of poured concrete, 6 in. thick.

3. Foundation work. The foundation shall be of poured concrete as above specified. All pilasters shall be of poured concrete and shall be left down to take care of the girders.

There shall be installed, in the top of the foundation, anchor bolts, size ½ in. by 10 in., with hook ends, and with nuts and washers. The bolts shall stick up 2 in. net and shall be placed about 12 in. back from each corner of the foundation and each opening in the foundation and otherwise about 8 ft. on center.

There shall be installed in the foundation wall, as shown, steel vents. These shall be with adjustable closers and 8 in. by 16 in. in size.

There shall be left an access door to the crawl space under the house. The jambs for this shall be of wood and shall be anchored to the foundation with anchor bolts. There shall be installed all around the top of the foundation a copper-faced-paper termite shield, 12 in. wide. This shield shall extend over the edge of the foundation at least 2 in. on each side.

4. Brick chimney, fireplace, and mantel. There shall be built a brick chimney, brick fireplace, fireplace hearth, and brick mantel. The mason contractor shall build these complete from the poured-concrete footings. The footings will be installed by others. All outside portions of the fireplace flue shall be of a good-grade face brick, to be selected by the owners. All other unexposed portions may be of a good-grade, hard, red common brick. There shall be built into the bottom of the chimney an ashpit, as shown. There shall be installed in this pit wall one 8 in. by 8 in. steel cleanout door. There shall also be installed in the bottom of the fireplace flue a cleanout door, steel, size 8 in. by 8 in. These doors shall be installed about 6 in. up from the grade line. All brick shall be laid up in natural-colored mortar with all joints completely filled with mortar and all joints tooled on the outside with concave surface. The flues shall be cement-plastered the complete distance from bottom to top.

There shall be installed at the top of the flues two flue liners, as shown. These shall be 12 in. by 12 in. The flue shall be completely capped except for the two liners. The capping shall form a washaway from the liners.

The chimney shall extend up at least 2 ft. above the highest ridge on the house and this distance shall not include the liners. A design or pattern shall be laid into the face of the chimney at the top, as shown. This pattern to be set out ½ in. When all brickwork is done, all exposed portions shall be washed down with acid and washed down with clean, cold water.

There shall be built one brick fireplace *mantel*. This shall be of a good-grade, uniform Red Roman brick, rock-face pattern, size 1⅝ in. by 3½ in. by 8 in. This brick to be laid up with white mortar and with ½-in. joints. This mortar shall be of white sand and white cement. The joints shall be tooled concave.

The fireplace opening shall be 36 in. wide and 30 in. high. There shall be installed here one cast-iron dome-type damper, with regulator, and one cast-iron ash dump in the hearth fireplace floor. The fireplace chamber shall be lined with regulation firebrick, laid up on edge with fire-clay mortar. There shall be installed two steel lintels, size 3½ in. by 3½ in., one for the brick jambs and one for the dome damper and common headers.

There shall be built a concrete *subhearth,* 4 in. thick, 18 in. wide, and 8 ft. long. This shall be left down to allow the red-tile hearth to finish even with the finish floors. (Wood floors to be ¹³⁄₁₆ in. thick.) The carpenters will form for the hearth, but the mason contractor will furnish and pour the hearth.

The finished hearth shall be laid with ½-in. by 6-in. by 6-in. hard-finish red-clay hearth tile. The hearth shall be three tile wide and 8 ft. long. These tile shall be laid in a bed of mortar not less than ½ in. thick and the exposed joints shall be laid in dark mahogany-colored mortar. When all hearth tile and mantel have been laid, they shall be cleaned with acid water.

The mason contractor shall furnish all *materials* and all labors to make and complete the above specified work. This shall include all bricks, tile, mortars, anchor bolts, angle irons, cleanouts, ash dumps, dampers, controls, wall ties, tools, scaffolding, etc., to complete the job. The chimney flashing will be furnished by others, but the mason will install it into the flues as the bricks are laid.

5. Carpentry work. The floor girders shall be built up of three 2- by 8-in. pieces spiked together, with all joints staggered. Spliced joints shall be made directly over the bearing posts.

All girders and all box sills shall have applied to them one coat of Terminix oil or equal for termite protection. The sills are to be treated with this before they are bolted down to the foundation.

All floor joists are to be 2- by 10-in. yellow pine or fir, spaced 16 in. on center. All floor and ceiling joists to be bridged with 1- by 3-in. or 2- by 2-in. fir. All ceiling joists shall be of sizes as shown over the rooms in the floor plan. All floor joists shall be doubled under all wall partitions.

All rafters to be 2- by 6-in. yellow pine or fir, spaced 16 in. on center.

All studding shall be full length and not spliced and shall be of 2- by 4-in. yellow pine spaced 16 in. O.C. All corner posts shall be of three-timber strength and not spliced. All frame walls shall have a single sole plate at the bottom and a double wall plate at the top.

All wall sheathing shall be ¾-in. by 2-ft. by 8-ft. insulite board or equal.

All roof sheathing and subflooring shall be ¾-in. square-edge yellow pine, 8 in. wide or equal.

All subflooring shall be covered with 30-lb. felt waterproof paper before laying any finish floor or floor coverings. All roof sheathing shall be covered with the same before laying any shingles.

Rooms to have tile- or linoleum-finish floor coverings shall have applied first, over the subfloor, ⅝-in. waterproof plywood sheets well nailed.

There shall be an excess opening to the crawl space under the house made from the garage, as shown. This opening shall have a wood frame or jambs, and shall be fitted with a removable door.

All external walls of the house shall have diagonal 1- by 4-in. braces let into the face of the studs at approximately 45 degrees and, wherever possible, shall extend from the sole plate at the bottom to the double wall plates at the top and shall be securely nailed to each stud and to the plates. The tops of all bearing posts shall be fitted with one piece of plate steel, size ½ by 8 by 16 in.

All outside trim shall be of white pine or equal and shall be primed with white-lead paint as soon as it is nailed or set into place.

All outside walls to be finished with ¾- by 10-in. beveled white-pine or redwood siding. This shall be nailed on with 8*d* galvanized box nails. All outside and inside corners of this siding wall shall have metal corners applied.

Purlins shall be installed under all common rafters and under all hip and valley rafters.

Vents shall be installed around the house in the cornice, in the soffit. These shall be 8 in. wide and 16 in. long and shall be bound with wood screen mold and covered with No. 16 mesh copper or bronze screen wire.

6. Roof work. All roof sheathing shall be covered with 30-lb. felt waterproof asphalt paper, lapped at least 3 in., before the shingles are applied. The roof shall then be covered with a good-grade asphalt slate-surfaced shingle, size 12 by 36 in., three in one, 210 lb. per square or equal. The colors are to be selected by the owners. The shingles shall be nailed on with 1¼-in. galvanized roofing nails, each shingle to have four nails, each about 1 in. above the shingle crotch. All hip and ridge shingles to be cut to 12 by 12 in. and nailed on with the same exposure as the rest of the shingles, regular exposure to be 5 in., all valleys to be laced. The shingle pattern shall be broken on halves and shall be vertical. Shingles are not to be applied at a time when the weather is so warm as to cause the slate to slip from working conditions.

7. Millwork. All inside woodwork, door trim, window trim, baseboard, etc., to be narrow line, as shown in the details. All window and door trim to have mitered joints at the tops. All woodwork to be of white pine. It shall be finished as stated under "20. Painting and finishing."

All inside doors to be hollow-core slab doors, birch on two sides, 1⅜ in. thick and 6 ft. 8 in. high. The three exterior doors shall be alike, birch on the inside and white pine on the outside. They shall be of the patterns shown, 1¾ in. thick, and installed with three 4-in. butt hinges each. They shall be 3 ft. wide and 6 ft. 8 in. high. All outside door entrances shall have oak threshold plates installed.

All windows to be Anderson Corp. or equal, factory-built units, preassembled with all-metal weather stripping, equipped with double-hung sash removable, storm sash removable, and screens. Patterns to be as shown. The center section of the picture windows shall have fixed sash and the upper and lower sections to have awning-type sash to swing out. These shall be equipped with screens.

Shutters shall be installed at the front of the house as shown. These shall be installed stationary. There shall be installed at each outside door a combination screen and storm door. This shall be fitted with all necessary hardware, hinges, locks, hooks, springs, etc.

There shall be built and installed in the hall, as shown, one double set of linen closets. These shall be of the built-in type, set into the wall and cased up with trim to match the rest of the woodwork.

There shall be built into the bathroom another double set of closets, as shown, and also one dressing unit with a Dresslyn lavatory. There shall be built into the dining-room space one china case, as shown.

The doors of all cabinets shall be of ¾-in. core stock with lipped edges and installed with ⅜-in. offset chrome-finish hardware, except in the kitchen (see "8. Kitchen cabinets").

There shall be installed at the garage one set of *garage doors*. These shall be of overhead design, four-panel—one with glass—wood doors. The doors shall be 1⅜ in. thick, 8 ft. wide, and 7 ft. high. The doors shall be installed with all necessary track, trim, hardware, locks, etc. The doors shall be fitted and adjusted for easy operation.

8. Kitchen cabinets. There shall be built and installed in the kitchen one set of wood cabinets of sizes and location as shown on the plans. The cabinets shall be made of wood and have all-wood doors and drawers. The doors shall be ¾ in. thick and made of five-ply core stock. The drawer fronts shall be of solid white pine. The sides and ends shall be of white pine and the bottoms shall be of ¼-in. fir plywood or pressed wood. The cabinet sections, both base and wall, shall have ¼-in. plywood backs. The base section shall also have ¼-in. plywood bottoms.

All material for these cabinets shall be of knotty-pine sound material and shall be finished natural (see "20. Painting and finishing"). The base section of the cabinets shall have built into it one double compartment flat rim kitchen sink (see "12. Plumbing installation"). The base section shall have the tops covered with a good grade of inlaid linoleum, installed with chrome-finish trim at the edges. (Owners request privilege of using Formica tops at extra cost to them.) All colors of linoleum or Formica to be selected by the owners.

All drawers and doors to be fitted with black-iron wrought hardware. All hardware to be selected by the owners.

9. Floors. All finish floors, unless otherwise stated, shall be of $^{25}\!/_{32}$-in. by 2¼-in. clear red-oak standard flooring, nailed down over a layer of 30-lb. felt waterproof paper. The flooring shall be nailed down with 8*d* case nails placed not more than 12-in. apart. The *kitchen, utility room,* and *bathroom* shall have a finish floor of 9-in. by 9-in. asphalt tile block laid over plywood, as previously stated. All colors of tile to be selected by the owners. All tile shall be installed by workmen of the trade and according to the manufacturer's directions. All rooms with tile floors shall have a rubber set on baseboard of colors to be selected. All other rooms, halls, closets, etc., shall receive the regular trim of baseboard, shoe, and mold.

All oak floors are to be sanded with a machine floor sander using three grades of sandpaper—coarse, medium, and fine—and shall have all the edges trimmed and finished and made ready to receive the filler, shellac, and wax (see "20. Painting and finishing").

10. Insulation. Insulation shall be installed over the entire attic area between the ceiling joists. This shall be of rock-wool batts or blanket, 3 in. or more thick. There shall be no insulation of any kind in the garage. The insulation need not extend out over the soffit in the attic as this would stop circulation. There shall be no insulation in the side walls of any kind other than that specified as follows: Install insulation under all rough window sills between the sills and the frame before the rock lath is applied.

11. Guttering. There shall be installed a complete job of guttering to take care of the water from the entire roof of the house. There shall be installed 5-in. eave troughs and 4-in. corrugated downfalls. All eave trough shall have mitered ends and square tubes. All eave trough shall be fully soldered both on the inside and on the outside at the joints.

All eave trough shall be painted with red lead or equal metal paint on the inside and on the back side next to the fascia boards before being installed. All eave trough shall be installed with sufficient drop to run the water off without standing in pockets. The eave trough shall be securely fastened to the house to prevent sags when the trough is loaded with water.

All downfalls shall be installed with elbows at the top and at the bottom. The downfalls shall be soldered to the hangers and fastened to the tubes at the top with metal screws. All elbows shall be soldered at all joints. There shall be galvanized strainers at all openings for each downfall. All downfalls shall be plumb and true. All guttering materials to be of 26-gage good-grade galvanized iron.

12. Plumbing installation. The following are general specifications in regard to the plumbing installation. Detailed specifications shall be left to the plumber. The plumber shall provide and be responsible for securing all necessary permits as and when needed for this work. The plumber shall provide all labor, materials, fixtures, trim, fittings, etc., needed to complete the job ready for use by the owners.

The water line from the corporation cock to the stop box shall be ⅝-in. lead pipe. From the stop box to the meter, it shall be of ¾-in. copper pipe. The water meter shall be installed in the utility room under the laundry tubs. The water line will enter the property from the boulevard on Finley St., and shall pass under the foundation and into the utility room. Provision shall be made for draining the entire system at some given point. All *water pipe* used on the job shall be copper and shall be installed with sweated joints.

The plumbing installation shall include a complete sewage-disposal system. The plumber will secure and provide all necessary permits for, and be responsible for, the opening and closing of the street for both sewer and water connections. The *sewer pipe* shall be of standard weight, 4-in. cast iron. All soil pipe shall be properly calked and leaded. The line from the street to the house shall have a drop of not less than ⅟₁₆ in. per ft. and not more than ¼ in. per ft. Differences greater than this shall be taken care of by the use of sharp-angle drops. The sewer and water lines will need to be laid up to the house at once so as not to delay other work in progress on the house.

A sill cock shall be provided and installed at a suitable location to provide water for other construction progress. All roughing in shall be done in cooperation with other workmen on the job at other trades, at a time necessary to prevent a stoppage, or holdup of other work on the house. All *waste pipe* shall be of proper size for the fixture used, and all fixtures shall be vented separately and fitted with cleanout plugs for easy access. A cleanout plug shall be left in the main line to the street and shall be accessible in the rear foundation of the house. Hot and cold water and disposal shall be installed in the utility room for an automatic washing machine and dryer. All of the following plumbing fixtures are to be supplied and installed by the plumber.

Install in the *bathroom* one 4 ft. 6 in. P-2225 T-Master Pembrook white-enameled cast-iron *bathtub,* right-hand drain, recessed and with B-158 mixing-valve combination, B-438 pop-up drain, and B-348 over-rim filler. The tub and trim to be American Standard or equal. Install on and over the tub, one *glass tub enclosure,* with sliding doors. Enclosure to be 4 ft 6 in. double Rollaway, No. 171A Permalume trim, Obscure glass. Enclosure to be by the Shower Door Co., America, or equal.

There shall be installed in the bathroom one *Dresslyn unit*. This shall be fitted with one 24-in. by 18-in. F-127-A Dresslyn vitreous china *lavatory*. This shall be installed with B-708-A combination fittings and drain, B-820 supplies to the wall with stops, 1¼-in. B-960, C.P. cast-brass P trap. Also furnish one pair No. 518 R and L union strips for the top. The lavatory shall be white and shall be American Standard or equal.

Install in the *bathroom* one *water-closet* No. F-2045 compact with C-214 white Church seat and cover. Same shall have supply to the wall and be equipped with a stop. The water closet shall be white and American Standard or equal.

There shall be installed into the kitchen cabinets in the *kitchen* one 32-in. by 21-in. P-7015-A Custom line flat-rim *sink*. It shall be of cast iron, acid-resisting white enameled. The sink shall have B-876-ST faucets and B-989 crumb-cup strainers with 1½-in. No. 2024 CP duo waste with a P trap. The sink will be fitted into the cabinet tops by the carpenters, but all other installation shall be made by the plumbers. The sink to be American Standard or equal.

There shall be installed into one compartment of the kitchen sink one General Electric *disposal* for garbage. This installation shall be complete and ready for use by the owners.

Laundry tubs shall be installed in the utility room as shown. This shall be No. P-7427 Bacon cast-iron, enameled sink and laundry tray combination, one-piece roll rim, with wall hangers and painted legs, P-7448-B. It shall have a B-906 S combination swinging-spout faucet with a lift-off soap dish. Also B-989 crumb-cup sink strainer.

A *water heater* shall be installed in the utility room as shown. This shall be a 42-gal. Spartan Continental natural-gas automatic water heater. Same shall carry a 10-year warranty. All controls shall be fully automatic. Heater to be National Continental or equal.

All plumbing work shall be done in accordance with city ordinances and shall be city inspected and approved. All plumbing work shall be done by and with licensed plumbers. The plumbing contractor shall guarantee his work and that of his employees and all materials used by him or them, for a period of one year from the date of the last payment or the final payment, against defective workmanship and materials.

13. Hardware. The contractor shall furnish, supply, and install all hardware for the entire job. This shall include all rough hardware and all finish hardware. Finish hardware shall include such items as door locks, door hinges, doorstops, window catches, window lifts, kitchen-cabinet hardware, linen-closet hardware, etc. All door hardware to be Dexter brand or equal.

All cabinet hardware to be chrome finish except the kitchen cabinets. These shall have black wrought iron. All regular doors shall have fitted and installed, three each, 3½-in. bright-brass butts to match the rest of the door hardware. All hardware to be installed properly for easy operation. Proper protection to be given all hardware to protect it from paint, varnish, etc.

14. Lathing. All rooms, closets, halls, and other areas to be plastered shall be lathed with rocklath. This shall be ⅜ in. by 16 in. by 48 in., perforated or equal. All lath to be properly spaced with staggered joints. No joints shall be left anywhere more than ¼ in. wide. All lath shall be nailed on with cement-coated lath nails, five nails to each joint. All bathroom fixtures to be grounded where needed before any rocklath or steel lath, cornerett, or corner bead is applied. All inside angles of all rooms, closets, etc., shall have applied full-length 3-in. by 3-in. steel cornerett. All outside corners of all rooms, halls, closets, etc., shall have applied full-length steel or metal corner bead. All chases and other openings made for any purpose shall be covered with steel plaster lath before plastering.

15. Plastering. Plaster the entire house of rooms, halls, closets, etc., unless otherwise specified. All plastering shall be of three-coat work or equal. All plastering to be done in white coat except that otherwise specified. Tile markings shall be optional with the owners. All plastered ceilings shall be level, and all walls and corners shall be plumb and straight. Methods should be used to prevent the plaster from drying out too fast, as this will cause the plaster to be weak and have cracks. All plaster mortar to be mixed outside the building.

At the completion of the work, the plasterer shall clean all surfaces of excess plaster and leave the floors broom clean.

All plastering shall be guaranteed, for a period of one year from date of the last and final payment made to him, against all defects in workmanship and materials used on the job.

16. Wiring and electrical work. There shall be installed a full and complete installation of house wiring, as specified below. These specifications shall be in general, and detailed specifications shall be completed by the electrical contractor. The contractor shall furnish all labor and materials to complete the work unless otherwise specified. All *wire* shall be nonmetallic sheathed cable (Romex). All wiring shall be concealed and all devices and circuits shall be completely polarized. All fixtures shall be secured to a switch or junction box. Other than bell wire where needed, no wire shall be used smaller than No. 12. The three outside doors shall be wired for *chimes.*

The *service entrance* shall be complete. The electrical contractor shall be responsible for all needed permits, make all connections, provide the meter and the installation for the same, provide for all inspections, and be responsible for their approval when and as needed. All service-entrance wiring shall be done in accordance with the National Underwriter's Code and shall meet the service-entrance requirements of the company furnishing the power and light. The service shall consist of 100 amps. min. 220 v. with an approved drop, meter, meter socket, etc., installed for combination service with range outlet and other heavy appliance outlets, including the heating unit. The service shall include one M.O. No. 12 add on breaker and cabinet with cover set flush with the wall. The breaker cabinet to be installed in the utility room. It shall be Cutler-Hammer or equal.

The *junction boxes* shall be galvanized steel, 3¼-in. or 4-in., as needed. All *switches* to be mercury type, Pass-Seymour or equal. All plates and convenience outlets to be the same and the same in color. All switches and outlets to be standard height from the floor.

The *circuits* shall consist of the following: No. 1 circuit, all illumination in the three bedrooms; No. 2 circuit, all illumination in the rest of the house; No. 3 circuit, all convenience outlets except the kitchen and the utility room; No. 4, all other convenience outlets; No. 5, the stove in the kitchen and the automatic water heater; No. 6, the heating system.

The *lighting fixtures* will be furnished by the owners, but shall be hung or installed by the electrical contractor. The contractor shall supply all fixtures with 75-watt Mazda bulbs. He shall supply all other materials, such as wire, hangers, boxes, switches, plates, receptacles, breaker box, chimes transformer, meters, bell wire, stove connections, furnace outlet or receptacle, service-entrance material, permits, etc., to make and complete the installation. A box and porcelain bulb holder shall be installed in the garage on switches, as shown.

The following *fixtures* will be furnished and delivered onto the job by the owners:

3 outside wall fixtures	1 dining-room fixture
2 hall fixtures	1 bathroom fixture
3 bedroom fixtures	2 bathroom wall brackets
2 kitchen fixtures	1 set of chimes
2 utility-room fixtures	

17. Heating plant. There shall be installed in the utility room one *gas-burning* furnace of forced hot-air circulation. There shall be used a *base figure* for the purchase of this plant, to include all labors and materials necessary for a complete installation ready for use by the owners. This figure shall be $1,100 (eleven hundred dollars). The owners will select the furnace and the dealer will need to meet the approval of the general contractor. The heating engineer representing the dealer shall present the owners with a general plan for the installation, showing the size of the furnace, location of all heat pipes, location of all cold-air returns, location of all register faces both hot and cold, and the size of same, total amount of heat loss for each room and for the total house, total c.f.m., and the total B.t.u. input and output of the furnace. The size of the furnace shall be figured on the basis of 70 degrees inside and zero outside. (Use National Warm Air and Air Conditioning Association calculation data.)

The *heat pipes* to be overhead in the attic and to be fully insulated. The *cold-air* pipes to be installed under the floor in the crawl space. Hot-air *register faces* to be installed in the walls, 6 ft. 6 in. high from the floor. Cold-air *register faces* to be installed in the baseboards. The *controls* shall be installed in the hall, with a day-and-night clock thermostat. The heating contractor shall be responsible for all wiring in regard to the furnace and shall pay for the same. This shall be on a circuit of its own, provided for this purpose.

The heating contractor shall be responsible for the gas piping, from the furnace back to the gas meter and from the gas meter to the outside of the foundation at the front of the house, and shall pay for the same. He shall make all connections for the same, test and make ready for use the heating system. All *gas controls* shall be fully automatic and the furnace shall be installed with a complete automatic humidifier.

The heating contractor and the general contractor shall jointly guarantee the installation of this furnace, for a period of one year from date of the last payment made to them, against all defective workmanship and materials.

18. Plastic tile. In the bathroom there shall be installed plastic tile, size 4¼ in. by 4¼ in., with a cove base and cap strip and a trim or feature strip in color. The tile shall extend up from the floor on the walls 4 ft. It shall be installed over the regular plastered walls. All tile shall be set plumb and true and according to the manufacturer's directions. All tilework shall be done by a workman of the trade.

All tile *colors* shall be selected by the owners.

The tile contractor shall guarantee his work and that of his employees for a period of one year from the date of his last payment received.

19. Driveway rock. There shall be built one crushed-rock driveway, as shown on the plans. This shall be of white limestone. Under the driveway approach there shall be laid 21 feet of 12-in. heavy-gage road culvert. The approach shall be built up of cinders to a sufficient grade to produce a driveway level and even with the finish grade of the yard. The driveway to be 10 ft. wide and from the garage to the street. There shall not be used less than 10 tons of good-grade, ⅜-in., white crushed-limestone rock, evenly spread and packed.

20. Painting and finishing. All woodwork, both inside and outside, shall be finished as follows:

All *inside doors* to be finished on both sides natural. This shall consist of one coat of clear sealer and two coats of satin varnish. Each coat to be rubbed down except the last.

All *outside doors* shall be finished on the inside the same as the other doors. The outside of these doors to have three coats of lead-and-oil paint, the same as the rest of the house.

All *cabinet doors* to be finished the same as the rest of the cabinets on which they are installed or, if linen closets, the same as the woodwork in the room.

The *garage doors* to be finished on both sides with three coats of lead-and-oil paint, the same as the rest of the house.

All *window sash* to be finished in three-coat enamel work. This shall consist of one coat of undercoater and two coats of enamel. The last coat of enamel should be full strength and not cut. All enamels to be Sherwin Williams or equal.

All *woodwork* and *trim* shall be finished in three-coat work of semigloss enamel, the first coat to be undercoater and the other two to be semigloss. The last coat shall be full and not cut.

All *linen closets, bookcases, kitchen cabinets,* etc., to receive the same finish as the rest of the room woodwork. All linen closets shall receive two coats of satin varnish on the inside. The kitchen cabinets shall not receive any finish on the inside except on the inside of the doors. These shall be finished the same as the outside of the doors.

All hardwood *floors* without covering shall be finished as follows: One coat of natural paste filler, one coat of white shellac or sealer, and two coats of Johnson's paste floor wax. The wax is to be well polished with an electric floor polisher.

All *walls* and *ceilings* of all rooms with sand-float finish plaster will receive three coats of flat wall paint. The first coat shall be wall primer and the next two shall be flat wall *oil paint*. The inside of all closets shall be finished the same as the room they are from.

The *walls* and *ceiling* of the kitchen, bathroom, utility room, and closets from, to receive three-coat work of enamel (gloss). This shall consist of one coat of under-coater and two coats of gloss enamel. The last coat to be full and nòt cut.

All of the above *colors* are to be selected by the owners and not applied without approval. The owners will come to the job at a time when the painter is ready and see the colors and make approval.

All *outside* woodwork, trim, siding, downfalls, gutters, metalwork, storm doors, screen frames, shutters, garage doors, etc., to be painted three coats of Dutch Boy white-lead-and-oil paint.

All *metalwork* to receive as its first coat a coat of red lead or equal of metal paint. All gutters shall be painted the same color as the rest of the house, the color of the shutters to be selected by the owners. After the first coat of paint has been applied and before the succeeding coat is applied, all nail holes, cracks, etc., shall be puttied smooth and full.

No painting shall be done on any surface until it has been properly prepared, and then only under conditions suitable for painting. All hardware, floors, glass, linoleum, tile, fixtures, etc., not intended to be painted shall be left clean and free from paint, filler, varnish, enamel, etc.

At the completion of the work, the painter shall retouch all damaged places, scratches, etc., that have occurred, finish all raw edges on doors at the top and bottom, and remove all paint on glass.

The painting contractor shall furnish all labors, materials, tools, scaffolding, etc., to complete the above work. This shall include all work that is commonly done by the painter.

The painter shall *guarantee* his work and that of his employees, for a period of one year from date of the last payment made to him, against all defective materials and workmanship.

21. Bids. The *owners* reserve the right to accept any bid and reject any or all bids.

10

PROJECTS, QUESTIONS, AND PROBLEMS

SUGGESTED PROJECTS

Many of the operations listed above cannot be taught successfully except on an actual building project. For this reason special effort should be exerted to secure this type of work for the building trades classes. Each boy should have a year's experience on a building if possible.

However, many of the above operations *can* be taught without a house or any building to construct. Following are a few suggested methods and projects for doing this:

1. The laying out and cutting of rafters can be taught on short pieces of 2 by 4's. The lines can be planed off later, and the same pieces used over again.

2. Framework may be taught by constructing small-scale frames from stock that has been scaled down to ¼ or ⅛ in. in size.

3. Window and door frames may be made to scale and taken apart to be used again.

4. Repair work on small buildings and garages also offers an opportunity for teaching the above operations.

5. Much valuable information can be gained from observation. Visit a house under construction and observe the actual work in progress.

6. Building projects such as the following will aid in teaching technical information, tool processes, and simple forms of construction not generally found in frame construction:

a. Sawhorses	*g.* Fences
b. Trellises	*h.* Gates
c. Workbenches	*i.* Garden furniture
d. Hog feeders	*j.* Window screens
e. Hog houses	*k.* Door screens
f. Flower boxes	*l.* Repair work

However, such work as plumbing a wall, bracing a house frame, setting window frames, door frames, and jambs, or fitting window sash can be taught only on an actual construction job.

QUESTIONS AND PROBLEMS

1. What tools are necessary for the building trades student to have and to use?

2. Name six common joints used in framing today.

3. Name three general types of framing and list their characteristics.

4. What are wall footings?

5. How is the length of a bearing post determined?

6. What is the purpose of foundation sills?

7. How are built-up girders generally made?

8. Describe the purpose of floor joists. How are they spaced?

9. Where are joist headers used?

10. What is a trimmer and where is it used?

11. Why are ceiling joists usually placed 16 in. on center?

12. Give five purposes of subflooring.

13. In what type of construction are floor plates used?

14. Where are double wall plates used?

15. What are studs and where are they used?

16. Show with a sketch how corner posts are made up.

17. Where are window headers used?

18. Why is it necessary to truss over wide openings?

19. What are the common sizes of wall sheathing?

20. Why is building paper so essential to good building?

21. Give the names of four kinds of felt and their weights.

22. What are rafters?

23. What determines the size of rafters?

24. How are rafters generally spaced?

25. What is meant by the term "rafter thrust"?

26. What are the four types of roof framing?

27. What is meant by the following terms: span, run, rise, pitch?

28. Give the rule for finding the rise of a roof.

29. Give the rule for finding the pitch of a roof.

30. List the principal roof pitches.

31. What does "length per foot of run" mean?

32. Give the rule for finding the number of inches rise per foot of run.

33. Name four kinds of rafters.

34. Describe the following terms: top cut, seat cut, length of rafter.

35. How do you find the length of a common rafter?

36. Lay out and cut a given top and bottom cut.

37. Why is it necessary to deduct for the ridge?

38. Describe the method for finding the length of hip and valley rafters.

39. How are side cuts obtained?

40. What are jack rafters?

41. Describe the methods used for finding the length of jacks.

42. How do you find the side cuts for jacks?

43. What is the length of a common rafter whose span is 24 ft., rise 8 ft., pitch $\frac{1}{3}$?

44. What is the length of a common rafter, span 24 ft., rise 12 ft.?

45. What is the length of a common rafter, span 20 ft., pitch $\frac{1}{3}$?

46. What is the length of a common rafter, run 12 ft., rise 8 ft.?

47. What is the length of a hip rafter, span 24 ft., rise 12 ft., pitch ½?

48. What is the length of a hip rafter, run 14 ft., pitch ⅓?

49. What is the length of a first jack on a roof, span 24 ft., pitch ⅓?

50. What is the length of the second jack? The length of the third and the fourth?

51. How many common, how many hip, how many jack rafters are needed for a building with a hip roof, size of building 16 ft. wide, 24 ft. long? Give the length of each rafter.

52. What is the purpose of wood shingles?

53. In what sizes are wood shingles manufactured?

54. Name three kinds of roof shingles and give their sizes.

55. Describe the correct method for laying on roll roofing.

56. What is meant by the term "square of roofing"?

57. How is the amount of roofing determined for a shed-type roof?

58. How is the amount of roofing determined for a gable roof?

59. How is the amount determined for a hip roof?

60. How many squares of shingles will be needed for a shed roof, run 12 ft., length of building 20 ft., and pitch ¼?

61. Where are wall shingles used?

62. Name three kinds of wall shingles.

63. Name two general kinds of wall siding.

64. What are corner boards?

65. What are metal siding corners?

66. For what purpose are plaster grounds used?

67. Why is it necessary to mark stud positions before plastering?

68. Name three general kinds of laths.

69. Where is corner bead used? Give its purposes.

70. What do we mean by "inside finish"?

71. Name seven kinds of inside finish.

72. How is flooring classified?

73. What is meant by the term "quartersawed lumber"?

74. What is meant by the term "slash-sawed lumber"?

75. Name the parts of the cornices.

76. Name the parts of a house that usually make up the "outside finish."

77. What are stairs?

78. What is meant by "treads" and "risers"?

79. Give the first steps used in constructing any stairs.

80. How do we determine the number of treads and risers needed?

81. Where are dormer windows used?

82. What are check rail windows?

83. How are sash classified?

84. How should window sash be fitted?

85. Describe the three grades of window glass.

86. How is glass manufactured?

87. Give the correct procedure for glazing a glass.

88. What is putty? How is it made?

89. Describe five general types of doors.

90. In what manner are doors graded?

91. Give the eight steps used in fitting a door.

92. Describe how to hang and hinge a door.

93. What is the purpose of insulation?

94. How may heat losses be prevented?

95. List as many different kinds of insulation as you can.

96. Describe yard lumber.

97. List the common defects and blemishes usually found in wood.

98. What is meant by the following terms: board feet, linear feet, rough stock, dressed lumber, S. 2 S., S. 4 S., surfaced, jointed lumber, lumber, timber, planks, boards, strips, scantlings, and standard lengths?

99. Give the rule for finding the number of board feet in a piece.

100. How many board feet of lumber in a piece, 1 in. thick, 12 in. wide, and 5 ft. long?

101. How many board feet in a piece, 1½ in. thick, 11 in. wide, and 16 ft. long?

102. A piece 10 ft. long, 2 in. thick, and 11 in. wide contains how many board feet of lumber?

103. How many board feet in a piece 2 in. thick, 8 in. wide, and 14 ft. long?

104. How many board feet of lumber in the following: 124 pieces, 2 in. thick, 10 in. wide, and 16 ft. long?

105. Name two types of scaffolds.

106. Describe the essentials of good scaffolding.

107. Describe suspended scaffolds.

108. Describe fixed scaffolds.

109. Describe horse scaffolds.

110. Where are rolling scaffolds used?

111. What are safety laws?

112. List 10 safety precautions that all carpenters should employ at all times.

113. Why is it so essential to be able to read blueprints?

114. What are views?

115. How is a view obtained?

116. What is meant by a front view?

117. What are elevations on a house plan?

118. How are elevations obtained?

119. What is the difference between a plan and an elevation?

120. Name the three general groups into which house plans may be divided.

121. What is the purpose of a plot plan?

122. Why is a roof or framing plan necessary?

123. Details serve what purpose in a set of house plans?

124. What is meant by cabinet details?

125. Why are symbols necessary in a set of house plans?

126. Indicate with a sketch the symbols for the following: wood, concrete, tile, brick, stone, earth.

127. What are the dimensions on a set of plans?

128. What are specifications and for what purpose are they?

129. What are the advantages to the contractor in using specifications?

130. What are the advantages to the home builder?

LIST OF VISUAL AIDS

The motion pictures and filmstrips listed in this *visual bibliography* can be used to supplement the material presented in this book. It is recommended, however, that each film be reviewed before using in order to determine its suitability for a particular group.

Both motion pictures and filmstrips are included in this visual bibliography, and the character of each is indicated by the self-explanatory abbreviations "MP" and "FS." Immediately following this identification is the name of the producer; and if the distributor is different from the producer, the name of the distributor follows the name of the producer. Abbreviations are used for names of producers and distributors, and these abbreviations are identified in the list of sources at the end of the bibliography. In most instances, the films can be borrowed or rented from local or state 16mm film libraries. (A nationwide list of these local sources is given in *A Directory of 2002 16mm Film Libraries,* available for 30 cents from the Superintendent of Documents, Washington 25, D.C.) Unless otherwise indicated, the motion pictures are 16mm, sound, black-and-white films and the filmstrips are 35mm, black-and-white, and silent.

For the convenience of film users, the films have been grouped by the subjects treated in various chapters, but in some instances the same film may be used in connection with several different chapters.

This bibliography is suggestive only, and film users should examine the latest annual edition and quarterly supplements of *Educational Film Guide,* a catalog of some 10,000 films published by

The H. W. Wilson Co., New York. The *Guide*, a standard reference book, is available in most college and public libraries.

GENERAL

ABC of Hand Tools (MP 2 parts GM 18min each color). Part 1 covers the use and care of hammers, screw drivers, pliers, and wrenches. Part 2, the use and care of files, saws, chisels, planes, and punches.

Care and Use of Hand Tools (MP series USA/UWF or Proto 10–20min each). Six films showing the proper uses of common tools. Titles and running times of the individual films are:

Bars, Punches, and Drifts (15min)	*Hammers* (11min)
Chisels (12min)	*Pliers and Screwdrivers* (15min)
Hacksaws (18min)	*Wrenches* (19min)

The Carpenter (MP Hutcheson 52min color). Reviews the many kinds of jobs performed by carpenters and explains the training procedures in preparing apprentices.

My Father's House (MP Gypsum 50min color). Shows the steps in remodeling a farm house, including erection of new walls and application of wallboard, flooring, siding, and roofing.

Woodworking (MP series USOE/UWF). Series of 20 motion pictures, each with a correlated filmstrip, same titles, covering operations on such power tools as the wood lathe, sander, shaper, and surfacer. Titles and running times are:

Operations on the Wood Lathe
No. 1 *Turning a Cylinder Between Centers* (17min)
No. 2 *Turning Taper Work* (12min)
No. 3 *Turning Work on a Face Plate* (15min)
No. 4 *Turning Work in a Chuck* (15min)
No. 5 *Face Turning a Collar* (16min)
Operations on the Sander
No. 1 *Sanding Flat and Irregular Surfaces* (19min)

Operations on the Jointer
No. 1 *Jointing Edges and Ends 90 Degrees to Face* (17min)
No. 2 *Beveling, Stop Chamfering, and Tapering Square Stock* (20min)
No. 3 *Face Planing Uneven Surfaces* (13min)
No. 4 *Jointing an Edge for Gluing: Installing Knives* (21 min)
Operations on the Band Saw
No. 1 *Sawing with Jig and Changing Band* (20min)
No. 2 *Sawing a Reverse Curve and a Bevel Reverse Curve* (18min)
Operations on the Variety Saw
No. 1 *Ripping and Crosscutting* (19min)
No. 2 *Beveling, Mitering, Rabbeting, and Dadoing* (19min)
No. 3 *Cutting Tenons and Segments* (15min)
No. 4 *Cutting Cove Molding and a Corebox* (19min)
Operations on the Spindle Shaper
No. 1 *Rabbeting and Shaping an Edge on Straight Stock* (18min)
No. 2 *Shaping After Template and Shaping Curved Edges* (17min)
No. 3 *Cutting Grooves with Circular Saw Blades* (22min)
Operations on the Single Face Surfacer
No. 1 *Planing Rough Surfaces to Dimensions* (17min)

Woodworking Machines (FS SVE 42 fr). Explains the uses of such machines as the lathe, drill press, sander, shaper, circular saw, band saw, and jointer.

1. FRAMING

Foundations and Concrete (MP USN/UWF 26min). Presents a brief overview of building foundations, usually made of concrete; and mentions variables which determine type of foundation to be used. (Building Techniques series.)

Framing: Floor Joists and Walls (MP USN/UWF 25min). Procedures for constructing walls, floors, doors, and windows of a two-story building. (Building Techniques series.)

2. RAFTER FRAMING

Framing: Hip and Valley Rafters (MP USN/UWF 25min). Shows how to cut, measure, and fit hip and valley rafters, and compares them with regular type rafters. (Building Techniques series.)

Framing: Rafter Principles and Common Rafters (MP USN/ UWF 15min). Laying out and cutting of rafters. (Building Techniques series.)

Teco Trussed Rafters (MP Timber Eng 18min silent). Demonstrates the planning, engineering, and organization of a large multiple unit dwelling project in which this roof truss was used.

3. ROOFING AND SIDING

According to Plan (MP Asbestos 14min color). Presents examples of how asbestos-cement sidewalls are used in the exterior of houses. Intended for builders, contractors, and architects.

Outside Story (MP Gypsum 25min color). Covers the history, production, and use of asphalt shingles in the roofing of private dwellings. Intended for technical schools and persons in the building trade.

5. FINISH—TRIM, WINDOWS, AND DOORS

Doorway to Happiness (MP Fir Door 30min color). Shows brief scenes of logging, a description of the manufacture of doors and millwork, and an explanation of how doors should be used and cared for in homes.

Fundamentals of Stair Layout (MP USN/UWF 11min). Covers the measuring, fitting, and installing of stairways. (Building Techniques series.)

How to Finish Plywood (MP Douglas 22min color). Demonstrates the finishing of plywood including painting, staining, enameling, and wallpapering.

Interior and Exterior Trim (MP USN/UWF 12min). Covers the installation of doors and windows and the finishing trim around them. (Building Techniques series.)

6. GLASS—GLAZING—INSULATION

The Professor Was a Salesman (MP Ins Bd Inst 38min color). Shows the sources and manufacture of structural insulation board, demonstrates its application and its uses, both in new construction and in remodeling.

The Story of Rock-wool Home Insulation (MP USBM 25min). Explains the causes of drafts and heat loss in homes and the value of insulation. Shows the manufacture of rock-wool insulation and the installation of such insulation in homes. (Sponsored by Johns-Manville Corp.)

Within These Walls (MP Gypsum 35min color). Reviews the history of insulation; points out the benefits of insulation in present-day homes; and shows how rock wool is manufactured.

8. SCAFFOLDS AND SAFETY MEASURES

Ladders, Scaffolds, and Floor Openings (MP Aetna 9min color). Shows the proper construction of ladders, scaffolds, and guards for floor openings; gives suggestions for their use and maintenance; and emphasizes the need for safe working habits in the construction field.

Safety Know How in the Workshop (FS SVE 55 fr). Explains the importance of safety in using woodworking tools.

9. BLUEPRINTS AND SPECIFICATIONS

Mechanical Drawing (MP series McGraw). Series of 8 motion pictures and 7 correlated filmstrips on the basic principles of drawings and blueprints. Titles and running times are:

Language of Drawing (10min)	*Shop Procedures* (17min)
Shape Description, Part 1 (11min)	*Sections* (10min)
Shape Description, Part 2 (8min)	*Auxiliary Views, Part 1* (11min)
	Auxiliary Views, Part 2 (10min)
	Size Description (13min)

DIRECTORY OF SOURCES

Aetna—Aetna Life Affiliated Companies, 151 Farmington Ave., Hartford 15, Conn.

Asbestos—Asbestos-Cement Products Assn., 509 Madison Ave., New York 22, N.Y.

Douglas—Douglas Fir Plywood Assn., Tacoma Bldg., Tacoma, Wash.

Fir Door—Fir Door Institute, Rust Bldg., Tacoma, Wash.

GM—General Motors Corp., 3044 W. Grand Blvd., Detroit 2, Mich.

Gypsum—United States Gypsum Co., 300 W. Adams St., Chicago 6, Ill.

Hutcheson—M. A. Hutcheson, 222 E. Michigan St., Indianapolis, Ind.

Ins Bd Inst—Insulation Board Institute, 111 W. Washington St., Chicago 2, Ill.

McGraw—McGraw-Hill Book Company, Inc., Text-Film Dept., 330 W. 42nd St., New York 36, N.Y.

Proto—Proto Tools, Box 3519 Terminal Annex, Los Angeles 54, Calif.

SVE—Society for Visual Education, 1345 W. Diversey Pkwy., Chicago 14, Ill.

Timber Eng—Timber Engineering Co., 1319—18th St., N.W., Washington 6, D.C.

* USA—U.S. Department of the Army, Washington 25, D.C.

USBM—U.S. Bureau of Mines, 4800 Forbes St., Pittsburgh, Pa.

* USN—U.S. Department of the Navy, Washington 25, D.C.

* USOE—U.S. Office of Education, Washington 25, D.C.

UWF—United World Films, Inc., 1445 Park Ave., New York 29, N.Y.

* Films distributed by United World Films, Inc.

INDEX